The Gene Concept

Selected Topics in Modern Biology

SERIES EDITOR

Professor Peter Gray
Andrey Avinoff Distinguished Professor of Biology
University of Pittsburgh

Series Editor's Statement

This is a background book which lays stress on the historical foundations of genetics. Its purpose is to arm the student who will be exploring other emerging aspects of genetics in his introductory biology course with a proper perspective of the subject.

The student first meets Mendel, not as an abstract, but as a human being; his experiments are given in his terms, and the student then follows, on an historical basis of personality and experiment, the subsequent history of genetics until the introduction of the fruitfly. This form is followed from Morgan until the 1920's when the discussion changes to mutations, both naturally and artificially induced. This leads naturally to micro-organisms, biochemical genetics, and, of course, at the end, the contemporary story of RNA and DNA. A brief final chapter emphasizes the role of genetics in contemporary society.

The Gene Concept, through its logical, historical discussion, its clear illustrations, and its list of supplementary reading in a wide field of genetics, offers to the interested beginning student an admirable opportunity, both to broaden his horizons and to augment his knowledge.

PETER GRAY

The Gene Concept

California State College at Fullerton
Fullerton, California

REINHOLD PUBLISHING CORPORATION
A subsidiary of Chapman-Reinhold, Inc.
NEW YORK   AMSTERDAM   LONDON

To My Parents
Who Supplied the Genes

Preface

Genetics is a young biology—indeed it is only sixty-five years old. In that short time many facts and ideas have developed, too many to be included in a brief introduction.

Any field of intellectual endeavor has its own history and methods. Rather than attempting to give all the facts of genetics, this book describes the past and present of genetics. Selected experiments are discussed in some detail to illustrate the changing methods and ideas of geneticists and the dependence of these ideas upon previous experiments and interpretations. In this way it is hoped that insight into the working world of biologists and the continuing evolution of a discipline may be gained.

NATALIE BARISH

Pittsburgh, Pennsylvania
May, 1965

Contents

chapter one

Mendel and His Famous Peas

Gregor Mendel, the "Father of Genetics," is a name familiar to many. This Augustinian monk, working by himself in a small garden in Brünn, was able to accomplish what many others before him had been unable to do. Truly fascinating are the reasons for his success in discovering some of the basic laws of heredity.

As soon as man began to use his eyes and head, he must have realized that "like begets like"—that humans bear humans and cats have kittens. By their very nature, man, or at least many men, are curious and desire meaningful explanations of what they observe. Humans have probably wondered about heredity for many centuries.

More significant than this is the early improvement of domestic plants and animals by breeding methods. On a tomb at Beni Hasam, Egypt, dated 1900 B.C. is a model of a greyhound, obviously not a wild dog but the result of careful selective breeding. Now, the intriguing question is: "What did Mendel do differently from others which made him successful in his search?"

Consider yourself faced with the essential question, "How can any regularities about heredity be discovered?" Naturally one needs to know both parents and offspring. "But what should be used?" Mendel gives his basis for choice:

The value and utility of any experiment are determined by the fitness of the material to the purpose for which it is used, and thus in the case before us it cannot be immaterial what plants are subjected to experiment and in what manner such experiments are conducted.

The selection of the plant group which shall serve for experiments of this kind must be made with all possible care if it be desired to avoid from the outset every risk of questionable results.

Mendel decided that he needed to have plants which had definite and differing characteristics that were constant and obvious. One can reach no conclusions about the inheritance of eye-color if everyone is blue-eyed; there must be contrast. This may seem obvious but one of the difficulties of many of Mendel's predecessors was they attempted to draw conclusions by looking at the total array of characteristics, rather than specific, clear-cut ones.

Next, one requires offspring of definite parents and many offspring. The value of the latter will be clear when the actual results of some of Mendel's experiments are presented. The former aspect is one main reason for using pea plants. They are constructed in such a way (see Fig. 1-1) that the reproductive organs are completely surrounded by petals. These organs mature before the flower opens so that normally self-fertilization occurs. Controlled artificial cross-fertilization can be done relatively easily. As for many offspring, every pea in every pea pod of a plant is the result of the fertilization of an egg. If one is observing a characteristic of the pea (seed) such as a wrinkled coat, the results are readily available. One disadvantage in observing a characteristic of the adult plant, such as the length of stem, is that the peas must mature before the results can be noted.

Mendel's paper, "Experiments in Plant Hybridisation,"

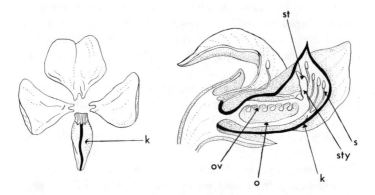

FIGURE 1-1. The flower of a pea. k, keel; ov, ovule; o, ovary wall; st, stigma; s, stamen; sty, style. (Redrawn from Robbins, Weier, and Stocking, *Botany, An Introduction to Plant Science*, Wiley, New York, 1964.)

1865, describes eight years of careful work. From a study of this paper one can discover the reasons for his success. One thing is obvious: Mendel planned his experiments carefully and wisely before he did them.

Mendel had a variety of pea plants which "bred true." He carefully raised these various types for two years before he experimented, to be sure that the offspring were constantly like the parents and that accidental cross-pollination did not occur.

Then Mendel made controlled matings, classifying parents and offspring with respect to specific, constant, and identifiable characteristics including distribution of flowers on the stem, color of unripe pod, and the shape of pods and seeds. He also did two other things to further insure meaningful results, both of which were time-consuming but important. Fortunately, he was able to obtain several varieties of pea plants which differed from each other with respect to these specific traits. Wisely, he raised more than one generation of pea plants, including mating the offspring of the initial parents, and he classified and *counted all offspring of every experiment,* making a statistical analysis possible. He points out that this had not been done previously. Instead, biologists of this period, interested in the origin of species, looked for naturally occurring crosses of species differing in *many* respects and reached *general* conclusions as to whether the offspring as a whole resembled one parent more than the other.

For simplicity, the results of only one set of matings involving one pair of contrasting characteristics will be presented, although Mendel used a total of seven different pairs of traits. Some plants have peas which are smooth and round; others have distinctly different angular and wrinkled seeds. When two such plants known to come from many generations of like parents were crossed (F_1), the resulting offspring (*hybrid* is the term used by Mendel) resembled only one of the parents. In this case all hybrid seeds were round. Similar results were obtained with all seven characteristics tested, i.e., the hybrids resembled one of the parents and not the other, the same characteristic appearing regardless of whether the male or female parent had that trait.

Now Mendel planted these seeds, allowed self-fertilization to occur and observed the characteristics of the seeds produced, now referred to as the *second filial generation* or F_2. The fact that Mendel made 253 such matings of the F_1 (hybrid) plants indicates the thoroughness of his work. He obtained the results shown in Table 1-1.

About one-fourth of the offspring are wrinkled, *unlike* their parents but *like* one grandparent; and about three-fourths are like the hybrid parents. Again similar results were obtained with all seven characteristics. In every case

TABLE 1–1

Plant #	Form of Seeds		Ratio of Round to Wrinkled
	# Round	# Wrinkled	
1	45	12	3:75:1
2	27	8	3.37:1
3	24	7	3.43:1
4	19	10	1.90:1
5	32	11	2.91:1
Total of 5 plants:	147	48	3.06:1
Total of all plants:	5,474	1,850	2.96:1

the relative proportions of the two groups were closer to 3:1 when large numbers of offspring were counted.

Now is the time to examine the results and to decide what conclusions can be drawn; for two important mental activities of a scientist are planning what to do and then deciding the significance of the results. One of the first generalizations Mendel made was that in each of the seven sets of traits, the hybrids of the initial crosses are like one or the other parent, not both and not in-between. Mendel designated the trait that was expressed in the hybrids as the *dominant* trait and the one that did not appear in the F_1 generation as being *recessive*. This aspect was very helpful in further analysis of these results. In the case of some characteristics, however, the F_1 offspring may be unlike either parent and the importance of dominance and recessiveness has decreased in recent years.

It is significant that the F_2 plants showing the recessive trait look exactly like the original parent #2. This indicates that whatever causes this trait has not changed in spite of not being expressed among the F_1 plants. Thus a factor or *gene* (a term introduced in 1909 by Johannsen) which some-how results in a specific characteristic is transmitted from

Summary of Results

Parent #1	×	Parent #2
(dominant trait)	↓	(recessive trait)

F_1 hybrids all like #1

$$F_1 \times F_1$$
↓

F_2: about 3/4 like #1 and about 1/4 like #2

one generation to the next and in such a way that a specific proportion having the trait is consistently found.

The *simplest* approach is to assume that each individual has one such factor which is transmitted through its gametes (the only physical link between generations) to its offspring. It is clear that simple though this may be, it cannot explain all the results. According to this scheme, parent #1 has a factor A; parent #2 another factor, a; F_1's have A like the dominant parent. But this does not explain how the F_2 offspring showing a recessive trait can have received an a factor if their parents are A.

The *next simplest* explanation is that all organisms have at least two factors all of which are given to the offspring. Then:

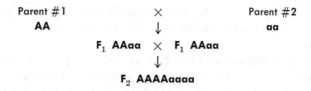

Parent #1   ×   Parent #2
AA ↓ aa

F_1 $AAaa$ × F_1 $AAaa$
↓

F_2 $AAAAaaaa$

This would explain where F_2 offspring could get an a factor but not how there could be different types in specific proportions. Also, if this idea were continued logically for several generations, the number of factors just involving one set of characteristics would increase rapidly (1, 2, 4, 8, 16, 32, 64, 128, 256, etc.) until eventually, if these factors had any dimensions at all, they would take more space than the organism itself.

The *third simplest* explanation is that each individual has two such factors, *one* of which is transmitted to any single offspring through the germ cells, which then unite at random. In this situation, parent #1 would be **AA;** parent #2, **aa** (both having come from many generations of plants like themselves). The hybrids would receive an **A** from parent #1 and an **a** from parent #2. Crossing or self-fertilizing these hybrids would mean mating an **Aa** individual with an **Aa** individual. If again we assume the simplest situation, that an egg or sperm is just as likely to have an **A** factor as an **a** factor, then one half the gametes would be of one type and the other half would be the other type. Since any one offspring results from the union of two gametes, one from each parent, one-half of the offspring will result from an **a** gamete, and of these receiving the **a** from one parent one-half also will receive an **a** from the other parent; that is, one-fourth of the offspring will be **aa** and show the recessive trait. This *does* fit our results explaining both how the recessive trait could arise *and* in what proportion. In the same manner, one-fourth of the offspring will be **AA** and show the dominant trait. Finally, the **A** of one parent will be together with the **a** of the other parent in one-fourth of the zygotes, *and* vice-versa; or one-half (one-fourth plus one-fourth) of the F_2 offspring will be **Aa** like their F_1 hybrid parents and show the dominant trait. Combining all the offspring expected to show the dominant trait (one-fourth plus one-half) we have three-fourths. This, too, fits the results. We can diagram this scheme as follows:

Parents:	#1: **AA**	×	#2: **aa**
Gametes:	all **A**		all **a**

F₁ all **Aa** (dominant trait expressed)

Gametes of **F₁**'s: 1/2 **A** ⟶ 1/2 **A**

1/2 **a** ⟶ 1/2 **a**

1/4 **AA**

3/4 dominant trait

F₂: 1/2 **Aa**

1/4 **aa** 1/4 recessive trait

Note that we have assumed that a *particulate* (indivisible and *unchanged*) unit or factor is being transmitted by each parent. This is one of the important conclusions made by Mendel. The fact that the recessive trait expressed by some of the plants in the second generation is just like that of one of the original types used but not found among the first generation of offspring supports this conclusion. Now we can state what is known as Mendel's first law of heredity: that with respect to one pair of factors these factors segregate in the gametes, any one gamete having one *or* the other, but not both. For clarity some of the more modern terms are: *genes* for factors, *alleles* or *allelomorphs* for a pair of factors, *genotype* for the genic makeup of an individual, and *phenotype* for the appearance of an individual.

There is a way by which the validity of these explanations can be checked. If you study the diagram above, you will see that some of the offspring showing the dominant trait have the same alleles, i.e., are *homozygous* for the **A** allele (**AA**), and that others having the same phenotype have one **A** allele and one **a** allele, i.e., are *heterozygous*. According to this scheme, one-fourth of all the **F₂** offspring, or one-third of those having the dominant phenotype are in the first group. If such plants were self-fertilized (**AA** × **AA**), one would expect *all* the offspring to have the dominant phenotype. The other two-thirds of the dominant F_2, although not distinguishable phenotypically from the first group, are heterozygous and if self-pollinated (**Aa** × **Aa**), the results expected would be the same as when F_1 individuals are crossed: 3/4 dominant: 1/4 recessive. Mendel completed such experiments and obtained just such results.

The obvious question that occurs to one is: "What happens when more than one set of traits is followed?" After all, organisms consist of many characteristics. Again Mendel was judicious and followed two sets of traits at a time, not all seven available. For example, when round (**AA**) peas which are also green (**bb**), previously found to be the recessive phenotype, were crossed with plants from wrinkled (**aa**), yellow (**BB**) seeds, all the offspring were round and yellow (**AaBb**) as would be expected. This also was the case if one parent was wrinkled and green, and the other round and yellow. Rather than allowing self-fertilization of such *di-hybrids,* if such plants are artificially mated with plants of the double recessive type (a test-cross), the results that might be possible are easier to discuss. The mating scheme is as follows:

Parent #1: **AABB**	×	Parent #2: **aabb**
(round, green peas)	↓	(wrinkled, yellow peas)

F_1: all **AaBb** (round, green peas).

F_1 **AaBb**	×	Double recessive: **aabb**
(round, green peas)	↓	(wrinkled, yellow peas)

??????????????

All the gametes of the **aabb** individual must contain an **a** and a **b** gene, for alleles segregate in gametes. It is not as obvious what type of germ cells are formed by the **AaBb** F₁ parent. There might be a relationship between the non-alleles such that whether a particular gamete has an **A** or an **a** allele is influenced by the presence or absence of one of the **B** alleles, or vice-versa. On the other hand, there may be no relation between the behavior of one set of alleles and the other set; that is, a germ cell is as likely to have the genotype **Ab** as the genotypes **AB,** or **aB** or **ab.** The combined results of two such experiments of Mendel are:

> 55 round, yellow
> 51 round, green
> 48 wrinkled, yellow
> 53 wrinkled, green

There are about equal numbers of each type. This is what we would expect if the germ cells formed by the dihybrid parent were in the following ratio: 1/4 **AB,** 1/4 **Ab,** 1/4 **aB** and 1/4 **ab,** all uniting at random with the **ab** gametes of the doubly recessive parent. Thus Mendel concludes that ". . . the relation of each pair of different characters in hybrid union is independent of the other differences in the two original parental stocks." ". . . the hybrid produces just so many kinds of egg and pollen cells as there are possible constant combination forms." Today this generalization, Mendel's second law of heredity, is often stated as "Non-alleles assort at random in gametes."

It is possible to predict what would be expected if two such dihybrids (**AaBb**) were crossed, or one self-fertilized, as was done in the first group of experiments involving one set of alleles or monohybrid crosses. In this case (**AaBb** × **AaBb**) each parent would form four types of gametes in equal numbers and the gametes of one parent would unite at random with the gametes of the other parent:

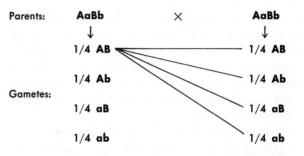

Parents: **AaBb**   ×   **AaBb**

A grid model (Punnett square) can be made filling in each square with the appropriate ratio and genotype of the offspring and adding all offspring of the same phenotype (Fig. 1-2). Filling in only those spaces which represent the

		Male Gametes			
		1/4 **AB**	1/4 **Ab**	1/4 **aB**	1/4 **ab**
	1/4 **AB**	1/16 **AABB**	1/16 **AABb**	1/16 **AaBB**	1/16 **AaBb**
Female	1/4 **Ab**	1/16 **AABb**		1/16 **AaBb**	
Gametes	1/4 **aB**	1/16 **AaBB**	1/16 **AaBb**		
	1/4 **ab**	1/16 **AaBb**			

FIGURE 1-2

union of two gametes that would result in offspring having both dominant traits, we find that 9/16 of them would be of this type. This group may be designated by **A-B-**, the - indicating that the second factors may be either **A** and **B** or **a** and **b**, respectively, resulting in the same phenotype in either case. If the rest of the combinations were completed, it would be concluded that 3/16 would be **A-bb**, 3/16 **aaB-** and 1/16 **aabb.** Although using the Punnett square method, as above, is fairly easy with two sets of alleles, one would have 4^3 or 64 squares to fill in if there were three sets of alleles and 4^4 or 256 squares when working with four sets of genes. Needless to say, this can be cumbersome and conducive to errors. If, however, these non-alleles do assort at random, one can determine the proportion of any genotype or phenotype readily by just remembering that for *each* pair of alleles, when F_1 hybrids are crossed, one expects the phenotypic ratio of 3/4 dominant: 1/4 recessive, and the genotypic ratio of 1/4 homozygous dominant: 1/2 heterozygous: 1/4 homozygous recessive. Notice that if the heterozygote differs from either homozygote in phenotype then the phenotypic ratio is the same as the genotypic ratio.

Just using the above information and having a cross of **AaBbCc** × **AaBbCc,** one can determine rather easily what proportion of the offspring would have the **A** and **B** dominant traits and the **c** recessive trait, for instance. One can draw the following set of conclusions: (1) that 3/4 of the offspring would have the **A** trait; (2) that 3/4 of those in number 1, or 9/16 (3/4 × 3/4) would have both the **A** and **B** traits; and (3) that 1/4 of those in number 2, or 9/64 (1/4 × 9/16) would have the phenotype **A-B-cc.** This same method can be applied to many situations, to find phenotypic or genotypic ratios or to find the proportion of a specific genotype or phenotype from a particular mating.

If Mendel had tried, as many before him had, to observe all characteristics at once in the offspring, he would have had difficulty. He used seven pairs of traits. If a plant heterozygous for all seven pairs of alleles had been self-fertilized, one would expect in the F_2 generation 2,187 (3^7) possible combinations of traits. Of these, only about 1/16,384 [$(1/4)^7$] would show all seven recessive traits. Mendel points out the improbability of being able to find any pattern in a small number of offspring using this approach and suggests this was one of the reasons for the lack of success of his predecessors.

By carefully planning his experiments, by being willing to undertake hours of tedious work, and by carefully analyzing his results, Mendel was able to make several important generalizations about heredity, i.e., that contrasting characteristics are the result of the presence of particulate units (genes) carried by an organism; that pairs of factors (alleles) segregate in gametes; and that unrelated factors (non-alleles) assort at random in gametes.

Although we look on Mendel's work as being a milestone in the history of biology, his contemporaries did not do so. Several factors probably contributed to this lack of recognition. With the publication of Darwin's "Origin of Species" in 1859, biologists were interested in natural crosses of plants which differed greatly from each other, not with constancy of characteristics and artificial matings. Mendel attempted to discover if his generalizations applied to other organisms. He had comparable results with beans and then made two unfortunate choices. Many species of hawkweed are known to occur in a great variety of types. For this reason and through the encouragement of Nageli, a prominent botanist, Mendel chose this plant for study. Unknown to botanists until 1904, many species of this plant normally reproduce *without* fertilization of the egg, i.e., apogamously, the offspring then being just like the "maternal parent." Thus no 3:1 or 9:3:3:1 ratios of F_2 hybrids occurred. Mendel also turned to bees, having raised them for many years in his gardens. Here too the biology of bees, including difficulty of controlling mating and development of some eggs without fertilization, hindered him from getting comparable results.

By some, Mendel might have been considered an amateur,

although a very capable one. He twice failed to pass examinations to be a full-time science teacher in high school. The first time he had had no formal training beyond high school himself, though no obvious reason for the second failure is available. He did act as a substitute teacher, which seemed to be pretty much a full-time job then, teaching mainly physics and some other natural science. Finally, when he was elected to be abbot of his monastery, a position he held until his death in 1884, his many duties, including a continued argument with the government about taxation, kept him from further research.

Toward the end of the 19th century many biologists again became interested in discovering regularities about heredity and in 1900 (considered to be the birth of genetics as a science) three biologists, von Tschermak, a German, de Vries, a Dutchman, and Correns, a Frenchman, independently found such regularities. They all discovered Mendel's papers, published 35 years previously in a rather obscure journal, and mentioned very briefly in one reference book, and gave credit where it was due.

chapter two

Exceptions and Explanations

It is a very exciting period when a science is young. So little is known that almost any research is fruitful in extending the application and meaning of the known, and in investigating apparent exceptions. After the rediscovery of Mendel in 1900, research took two main roads. One was continued controlled breeding experiments using many different plants and animals; the other, an attempt to discover where and what Mendel's "factors" were.

Mendel's conclusions were not immediately accepted as universal principles by everyone. Mendel himself had noted exceptions in his experiments with hawkweed. Criticism was particularly strong in England where there had been much discussion concerning the inheritance of continuously variable characteristics. Traits such as height show a great variety of expression among the members of a population. The study of the inheritance of such quantitative variables (Chapter 5) is fairly complex. Mendel had used characteristics with discontinuous variation, i.e., an individual pea was *either* smooth *or* wrinkled and all peas could be put into either category. Some biologists thought his conclusions to be quite limited in their application.

William Bateson, one of the early English supporters of

Mendel wrote: * "In many well-regulated occupations there are persons known as 'knockers-up' whose thankless task it is to rouse others from their slumber, and tell them work-time is come round again. That part I am venturing to play this morning, and if I have knocked a trifle loud, it is because there is need."

Bateson and others continued to use Mendel's methods and found similar results with a great variety of plants and animals and characteristics. There were differences, some not difficult to explain. For example, two different sets of genes affecting the same part of an organism sometimes result in F_2 phenotypic ratios other than the usual 9:3:3:1. Thus in rabbits a gene for grey color (**G**) is dominant to its allele (**g**) resulting in a black coat. Another set of alleles (**C** and **c**) either allows pigment to be produced or results in an albino rabbit, the latter trait being recessive. When animals heterozygous for both sets of alleles (**CcGg**) are mated, the phenotypic ratio is 9 grey: 3 black: 4 albino (Fig. 2-1) because all animals having the genotype **cc** are albino regardles of the **G** alleles.

A similar although somewhat more complex situation was discovered in sweet peas. Two sets of alleles again are involved, but whenever either or both pairs of genes are recessive, the flowers are white. When two white flowers having the respective genotypes of **CCrr** and **ccRR** are crossed, the F_1 flowers are **CcRr** and have color. The F_2 phenotypic ratio is 9/16 colored (**C-R-**) and 7/16 white (**C-rr, ccR-** and **ccrr**). The specific color of the flower depends on other sets of genes, one pair resulting in a purple or red.

Bateson found another and more puzzling situation with these same sweet peas. The plants were homozygous for the

* *Mendel's Principles of Heredity. A Defense.*, 1902 Cambridge University Press. p. xii.

Parents:	Grey (**GgCc**)	×	Grey (**GgCc**)
Gametes:	1/4 **GC**		1/4 **GC**
	1/4 **Gc**		1/4 **Gc**
	1/4 **gC**		1/4 **gC**
	1/4 **gc**		1/4 **gc**

F₂: 3/4 **G-** × 3/4 **C-** = 9/16 **G-C-**, Grey

3/4 **C-** × 1/4 **gg** = 3/16 **ggC-**, Black

3/4 **G-** × 1/4 **cc** = 3/16 **G-cc**, albino

1/4 **gg** × 1/4 **cc** = 1/16 **ggcc**, albino

FIGURE 2-1. Two sets of genes affecting same characteristic. The - in **G-** signifies that either allele may be present. Thus **G-** may be **GG** or **Gg**.

color genes but varied in the specific color, purple or red, and in the pollen shape, long or round. Typical 3:1 F_2 ratios were obtained when these two sets of unrelated traits were studied separately. The purple color and long pollen were the dominant characteristics. When plants heterozygous for both sets of alleles were crossed, however, the results were quite different from those expected, and not just some combination of the 9:3:3:1 ratio either (Fig. 2-2).

Obviously these data deviate markedly from the expected numbers. Purple, a result of a dominant gene, seems to associate with another dominant gene affecting pollen shape, and the two recessive traits are together more often than expected. Conversely, Bateson found some cases in which the dominant gene of one set of alleles seemed to associate with the recessive allele of another pair of genes. At first he

Mating:	F$_1$ purple, long (PpLl)	×	F$_1$ purple, (PpLl)	
Phenotype of F$_2$	purple, long	purple, round	red, long	red, round
Expected Proportion:	9/16	3/16	3/16	1/16
Expected Numbers:	240	80	80	27
Observed Numbers:	296	19	27	85

FIGURE 2-2. Bateson's exceptional results.

considered these two situations to be unrelated. Not until 1913, after carefully examining all these experiments, including the parents of the F$_1$, was he able to conclude that these two types of results were related. If the original parents were of the pattern **AABB** × **aabb** so that the F$_1$ offspring received the dominant alleles from one parent and the recessive alleles from the other parent, then the dominant traits were associated in the F$_2$ as in the example given. In contrast if the original parents were **AAbb** × **aaBB,** then the F$_2$ ratio indicated a dissociation of dominant traits, the two 3/16 groups having a number larger than expected.

Bateson was unable to find an acceptable explanation for these results although he tried for several years. He did realize that these data imply that the gametes produced by the F$_1$'s are not in equal numbers, **AB** and **ab** forming more often than **Ab** and **aB** in the first case and **Ab** and **aB** gametes being preponderant in the second situation. The necessary information was available to him, for in 1903 a young graduate student at Columbia University published a short but very significant paper. In this article Walter Sutton did not present numerical results of breeding experiments but noted similarities between conclusions made about *genes* from breeding experiments and conclusions made about *chromosomes* from direct observations of cells.

Microscopic examination reveals that cells have in their nuclei a specific number of pairs of long discrete structures called chromosomes. The number of chromosomes is constant for a given species: man having 23 pairs, crayfish 100 pairs, and and fruitflies 4 pairs. The two *homologous chromosomes* of a pair are alike in shape and size and maintain their identity during cell divisions.

An animal cell which forms gametes goes through the following events involving chromosomes. This process of *meiosis* (Figs. 2-3 and 2-4) includes two cell divisions so that the original cell results in four cells. Before the first division each chromosome duplicates itself, and homologous chromosomes come together or *synapse*. Non-homologs are lined up in the center of the cell but do not synapse. The cell divides into two cells, one of the duplicated chromosomes being in one daughter cell, the other in the other cell. Thus the two original chromosomes have segregated. In a subsequent cell division the duplicated parts separate. The final result is four cells each having *one of each pair* of chromosomes of the same shape and relative size as in the original cell. The total number of chromosomes per cell is now one-half of the original number. Careful observation of non-homologous chromosomes which are clearly distinguishable reveals that such chromosomes assort at random.

In male animals all four cells resulting from meiosis differentiate into sperm. In female animals one of the four cells is large and forms an egg; the other three are very small and disintegrate. The gametes of plants also have the same

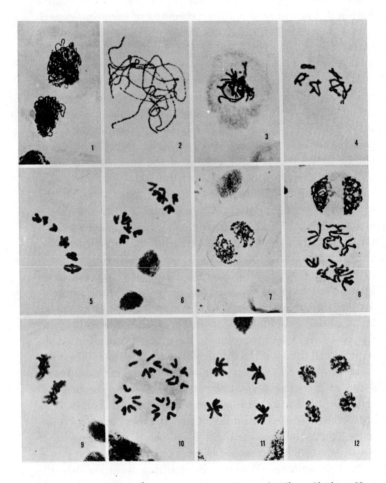

FIGURE 2-3. Stages of meiosis. (From Muhling and Wilson, Rhodora **63**: 267–275.)

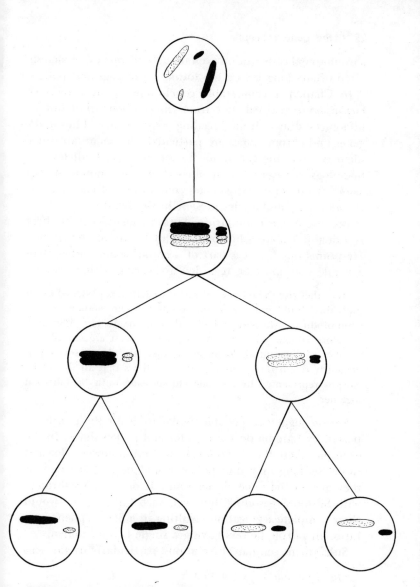

FIGURE 2-4. Diagram of meiosis. Black and stippled chromosomes of same length are homologs.

chromosomal constitution even though the process of meiosis often occurs long before the formation of eggs and pollen.

In Chapter 1 comparable conclusions about hereditary factors were reached, not from direct observation but as inferences drawn from breeding experiments. Thus *both* genes and chromosomes are particulate and maintain their identity from one generation to the next; *both* alleles and homologs segregate; *both* non-alleles and non-homologs assort at random; and gametes contain one of each pair of chromosomes and alleles present in the adult.

Because of such similarities Sutton concluded that there is a definite relationship between alleles and chromosomes. He points out * that a part of a chromosome, rather than a whole one, must be regarded as bearing a single allele:

... for otherwise the number of distinct characters possessed by an individual could not exceed the number of chromosomes in the germ-products; which is undoubtedly contrary to fact. We must, therefore assume that some chromosomes at least are related to a number of different allelomorphs. If then, the chromosomes permanently retain their individuality, it follows that all the allelomorphs represented by any one chromosome must be inherited together.

Sutton suggests a possible explanation for the results reported by Bateson on flower color and pollen shape. In the example given, the alleles for purple or red flower color and those for long or round pollen would be *linked* genes, as they are on the same chromosome. If one follows through with Sutton's reasoning, however, such linked genes would show complete segregation resulting in a 3:1 F_2 phenotypic ratio, all purple flowers having a single type of pollen.

Subsequent cellular observations, particularly by Janssens

* *Biological Bulletin,* vol. 4, 1903.

in 1909, indicated how linked non-alleles might result in a variety of F_2 ratios. During the synaptic stage of meiosis, homologous chromosomes become entangled and may break, exchanging parts before reuniting. If genes are on such chromosomes, they too will be exchanged. Thus if one starts out with a double heterozygote, $\dfrac{\mathbf{P} \quad \mathbf{L}}{\mathbf{p} \quad \mathbf{l}} \times$ ($\mathbf{P}$ = Purple; $\mathbf{p}$ = red; $\mathbf{L}$ = Long; $\mathbf{l}$ = round) a break and exchange between the $\mathbf{P}$ and $\mathbf{L}$ genes would result in *crossover* gametes, $\mathbf{Pl}$ and $\mathbf{pL}$. The majority of gametes would still be $\mathbf{PL}$ and $\mathbf{pl}$ if crossing-over was rare.

It is easier to see the effect of crossing-over on phenotypic ratios using a test cross of an F_1 individual to the double recessive organism than the mating of two F_1 dihybrid plants that Bateson had (Fig. 2-5). The majority of offspring would be non-crossovers: purple flowers with long pollen and red flowers with round pollen. If the F_1 parent were $\dfrac{\mathbf{P} \quad \mathbf{l}}{\mathbf{p} \quad \mathbf{L}} \times$, then the reverse results would be expected: purple flowers with long pollen and red flowers with round pollen being crossovers and in the minority. It also was supposed that the frequency of such crossover gametes depended upon the distance between the linked genes. The further apart the genes are the more frequently will the chromosomes break and exchange parts between them, producing more genetic crossovers.

Thus Bateson's results may be explained by adding the phenomenon of differential crossing over to the idea of linkage. Yet Bateson was very reluctant to accept such an explanation. As late as 1913 he wrote: "It is, in my judgment, impossible, as yet to form definite views as to the relations of the various parts of the cell to the function of heredity."

He instead suggested a complicated series of events occurring in embryonic cells prior to the formation of gametes to explain odd phenotypic ratios as 41:7:7:9 or 129:63:63:1.

Parents:	F_1	P	L	×	p	l	
		p	l		p	l	
		(purple flowers, long pollen)			(red flowers, round pollen)		
Gametes:	Majority Non-crossovers				All		
	P	L	and	p	l	p	l
	Minority Crossovers:						
	P	l	and	p	L		
Offspring:	Majority:						
	P	L	(purple flowers, long pollen)	and	p	l	(red flowers, round pollen)
	p	l			p	l	
	Minority:						
	P	l	(purple flowers, round pollen)	and	p	L	(red flowers, long pollen)
	p	l			p	l	

FIGURE 2-5. Effect of linkage on test-cross.

Perhaps his struggles to have Mendelian principles accepted in England made him reluctant to admit that random assortment of non-alleles in the formation of gametes was not universally true. Also a more abstract question may have influenced him. To accept the fact that genes are parts of chromosomes also means the acceptance of the gene as a truly physical and particulate entity. In the early 20th century and even today, it is difficult for many people to believe that a significant part of themselves is determined by chance arrangements of material entities. Bateson preferred not to commit himself although he speculated much about genetic behavior. He suggested that dominant alleles allowed certain enzymes to be produced which resulted in specific traits and that recessives were the result of the absence of such genes.

Perhaps Bateson would have been convinced that genes are located on chromosomes by an experiment with corn published in 1931 by Harriet Creighton and Barbara Mc-Clintock. This experiment was designed specifically to correlate cellular observations with breeding results. The experiment utilized a pair of morphologically different chromosomes with a homologous area capable of synapsis, and linked genes.

One chromosome was straight, the other had a knob on one end and was longer, both differences easily visible in a microscope. Previous evidence indicated two linked genes were located between the knob and the middle of the chromosome. These were a dominant gene (**C**) causing a color to be produced in a particular layer of the kernels; and a linked recessive gene (**wx**), causing a starch to be formed in the kernels which gave them a waxy appearance. The straight chromosome contained the alleles of these two genes: colorless (**c**) and normal starch (**Wx**). Using a dotted line to indicate non-homologous chromosomal material, the cross may be diagrammed:

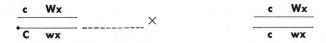

Chromosomal exchange results in knobbed, short chromosomes and long, knobless ones. Genetic crossovers in the doubly heterozygous parent results in colored, non-waxy

(**CcWxWx** or **CcWxwx**) kernels or colorless kernels, either waxy (**ccwxwx**) or non-waxy (**ccWxwx**). The most pertinent result was the observation that all plants with colored kernels, whether non-crossovers or crossovers, showed the presence of the knobbed chromosome. Those that were colored and non-waxy (crossovers) also were short. There was a direct and consistent correlation between visibly observable chromosomal exchange and genetic exchange inferred from breeding results. This was considered conclusive proof that genes are located in or on chromosomes.

Thus some of the "exceptions" to Mendel's laws do not necessitate abandoning these principles but lead to expansion and new insight in the young science of genetics.

chapter three

Fruitflies and Sex Linkage

What would constitute an ideal organism with which to study genetics? Man? Certainly not if one needs controlled matings and many offspring. Sweet peas? Perhaps. But remember the many years that Mendel worked to obtain his data. The common fruitfly, *Drosophila melanogaster* has played the leading role in the work of many geneticists. Advantages of using it are apparent with only a little knowledge of this fly: the generation time is about ten days and many offspring are produced. If one female and one male are used as parents, one may obtain 50–200 offspring. Relatively little space and money are required to raise fruitflies. They are kept in small tubes or in half-pint milk bottles with food in the bottom. Generally, they are given a mixture not unlike thick oatmeal containing corn meal, molasses, yeast and a thickening agent.

With a low-power microscope, many characteristics may be discerned: eye color and shape, wing form, various bristle patterns, body color, etc.; moreover, the sexes are easily distinguished. These general aspects led to the initial use of *Drosophila* in genetic research, but other discoveries about them and just the accumulation of genetic knowledge has increased their usefulness.

For example, their chromosome number is eight (four pair) and each pair can be distinguished by size or shape from the others. This small number is an advantage in itself. In 1933, many years after their initial use, it was discovered that the salivary glands of these flies in the larval or maggot stage had cells with very large chromosomes, 100–200 times longer and 1,000–2,000 times the volume of their ordinary chromosomes. Thus new research was possible using a well-known organism.

Early in the use of *Drosophila,* about 1909, a male fly with white eyes was observed. Normally the eye color is a brick red. Fortunately, this fly was isolated and the results of a series of crosses were reported by Thomas Hunt Morgan, the first geneticist to receive a Nobel prize. This white-eyed characteristic is called a *spontaneous mutation* (a sudden but stable change not the result of special treatment). Many mutations in fruitflies are now known.

When this white-eyed male was crossed with normal red-eyed females, all the offspring were red-eyed; and when F_1 hybrids were crossed, 3,460 red-eyed flies and 782 white-eyed flies were obtained. With this information, the results fit a typical Mendelian 3:1 F_2 ratio. But *all* the white-eyed flies were male and of the red-eyed flies 2,459 were female and 1,011 were males. This might suggest that only males can be white-eyed. However, when the white-eyed male was crossed with some of the hybrid daughters, the results were 129 red females, 132 red males, 88 white females and 86 white males. So females can have white eyes. These and other results of breeding experiments involving white and red-eyed fruitflies are summarized in Fig. 3-1.

One conclusion is clear. The heredity of white eye color is somehow related to sex. In the initial crosses (1a and 2a of Fig. 3-1), the phenotype of the male offspring is the same as

1a:
Parents: white male $\times$ red female

$\downarrow$

F_1: all red (both sexes)

1b:
Parents:
   F_1 red male $\times$ F_1 red female

$\downarrow$

F_2: 1/2 red females
        1/4 red males
        1/4 white males

1c:
Parents: white male $\times$ F_1 red female

$\downarrow$

        1/4 red females
        1/4 red males
        1/4 white females
        1/4 white males

2a:
Parents: white female $\times$ red male

$\downarrow$

F_1: 1/2 white males
        1/2 red females

2b:
Parents:
   F_1 red female $\times$ F_1 white male

$\downarrow$

F_2: 1/4 red females
        1/4 red males
        1/4 white females
        1/4 white males

FIGURE 3-1. Crosses involving red and white-eyed *Drosophila*.

the female parent. Note, also, that the results of the F_1 cross in 2b are the same as the results of the backcross given in 1c.

The final explanation involves a knowledge of the chromosomes of fruitflies, again a combination of direct observation and breeding experiments. In these and many other organisms, including man, one of the pairs of chromosomes are not always alike. In one sex, the female, they are alike; but in males the chromosomes of one pair definitely differ. In *Drosophila* one is much shorter than the other and it is bent. It is customary to call this the **Y** chromosome and its corresponding long chromosome, the **X** chromosome; the two collectively are the *sex chromosomes*. Females have two **X**'s and males have one **X** and one **Y**, always receiving the **Y** from their father and the **X** from their mother.

If it is assumed that the **X** chromosome, being longer, has genes not found on the **Y** chromosome, the above results become clear. Using **w** to represent a gene on the **X** resulting in white eyes and **W** for its allele resulting in red eyes, females genotypically may be **WW, Ww,** or **ww,** the first two resulting in red phenotype and the last resulting in white eyes, the recessive trait. This is similar to situations discussed in previous chapters. In contrast, there can be only two types of males genotypically, **W** and **w**, since they possess only one **X** chromosome. Phenotypically these result in red and white eyes respectively. Since only one gene is involved, a male cannot be described as being homozygous or heterozygous but is said to be *hemizygous*. Fig. 3-2 shows how this suggestion of *sex-linked* genes, that is genes located on the **X** chromosome, would explain the results given in Fig. 3-1. For example, since a female must have two **w** alleles in order to have white eyes (white being recessive) and one of these must come from her male parent, that parent will always be white-eyed.

Because of this unique pattern of inheritance, sex-linked characteristics are relatively easy to discover, even in man. Two well-known human traits of this type are hemophilia and complete color blindness. The pattern also indicates why these traits are rare in women. This is particularly true in the case of hemophilia, a condition which results in very slow clotting of the blood. Prior to the use of extensive blood transfusions and other medical treatments, most males died before maturity and so did not have daughters that might be hemophiliacs. Heterozygous women, or carriers,

1a:
Parents:

    white males × red females
       wY   **WW**

F_1:   **Ww** red females
       WY red males

1b:
Parents:

   F_1 red male × F_1 red female
     WY   **Ww**

F_2:   1/4 **WW** red females
       1/4 **Ww** red females
       1/4 **WY** red males
       1/4 **wY** white males

1c:
Parents: white male × F_1 red female
         wY   **Ww**

       1/4 **Ww** red females
       1/4 **ww** white females
       1/4 **WY** red males
       1/4 **wY** white males

2a:

    white females × red males
      ww   **WY**

       Ww red females
       wY white females

2b:

  F_1 red female × F_1 white male
     Ww   **wY**

    1/4 **Ww** red females
    1/4 **ww** white females
    1/4 **WY** red males
    1/4 **wY** white males

FIGURE 3-2. Sex-linkage inheritance of white eye in *Drosophila*. w = white, W = red, Y = Y chromosome.

do not have the trait, but one-half of their sons receiving the gene have hemophilia.

In some organisms, such as all birds and butterflies, it is the female which is hemizygous and carries only one sex-linked allele, the males being comparable to the female fruitfly. Sex-linked inheritance in these situations give the same type of results, except the role of the sexes is reversed.

If several such sex-linked characteristics in one organism are the result of genes located on the **X** chromosome, then these genes must be linked to each other, as described in Chapter 2. There are two important differences, however: the specific chromosome involved is known and if a male has only one **X**, and a female two **X** chromosomes, crossing over would occur only in females, making linkage studies easier. A curious fact, still to be explained, is that there is *no* crossing over between *any* of the four pairs of chromosomes in male fruitflies, again making this animal particularly favorable for research.

check out

In 1913, A. H. Sturtevant published the results of breeding experiments using six sex-linked traits in *Drosophila*. As discussed in Chapter 2, if crossing over is the result of an exchange of chromosomal material, then the further apart two linked genes are the more often crossing over can occur. Using more than two linked factors, a slightly different approach may be taken—that of determining the relative order of linked genes. With three such genes, **A, B,** and **C,** there would be more crossovers between the more distant genes. In addition, the amount of crossing over should be additive if linked genes are in linear order rather than in a circle, for example. That is, if the order is **B, C, A,** then the percentage of crossovers between **B** and **C** plus the percentage between **C** and **A** should be about equal to the percentage between **B** and **A**.

In a typical experiment, female flies heterozygous for the genes to be studied (**ABC/abc**) are mated with males having the traits which are recessive in the female. These males would transmit the **Y** chromosome with none of the genes to their sons and the **X** chromosome with all three recessive alleles to their daughters. The females would contribute one or the other of their **X** chromosomes to each offspring. If no crossovers between the **X** chromosomes occur, offspring receive either the **ABC** genes and have all three dominant traits or the **abc** genes being recessive for all three traits.

The results of crossovers occurring during meiosis in the formation of the eggs produced by the female are of particular interest. If the order of the genes is **A   B   C**, then a

crossover between the **A** and **B** genes would result in eggs having the genotypes **A b c** or **a B C**, these eggs being fertilized by sperm with **a b c** genes or a **Y** chromosome. Four types of offspring would result:

Female parent and location of crossover:	Genotype of Offspring:	Phenotype of Offspring:
A B C × a b c	A b c Y	**Abc** males
	A b c a b c	**Abc** females
Male parent a b c Y	a B C Y	**aBC** males
	a B C a b c	**aBC** female

Thus all **Abc** and **aBC** offspring are the result of crossovers between the **A** and **B** genes. In a similar manner, **ABc** and **abC** offspring represent crossovers between the **B** and **C** genes. Three of the six sets of genes used by Sturtevant gave the following data, using two pairs of genes at a time:

Type of Crossover	% of Crossovers
A-B	29.7
B-C	26.9
A-C	45.2

The largest percentage represents the more distant genes, and so the order must be **A B C** or **C B A**. Also **B** and **C** are closer to each other than **A** and **B** are since 26.9 is less than 29.7. But the sum of **A-B** crossovers and **B-C** crossovers (56.6%) is greater than the amount observed in a cross just involving **A** and **C** (45.2%). Part of this discrepancy can be explained by the occurrence of *double crossovers*. If a crossover occurs between **A** and **B** and simultaneously another one between **B** and **C** in a mating involving all three genes, the resulting offspring would be either **AbC** or **aBc** phenotypically and could be distinguished from the other groups. Such individuals would have to be counted as one crossover between **A** and **B,** as one crossover between **B** and **C** and as two crossovers between **A** and **C**. If one had a mating just using the **A** and **C** genes, such double crossovers phenotypically would be **AC** or **ac** and would be counted as *non-crossovers*. The crossover distance calculated would then be low.

The closer genes are, the less frequent such double crossovers occur. Again using data from Sturtevant, the following illustrates this point.

Type of Crossover	% of Crossovers
B-P	32.2
B-R	35.5
P-R	3.0

In this case, the order is **BPR** or **RPB** with the **P** and **R** genes quite close to each other, making the frequency of two simultaneous crossovers, one between **B** and **P** and another between **P** and **R**, very rare. Now the sum of 32.2 plus 3.0 equal to 35.2 is essentially that observed as being the cross-over distance between **B** and **R** (35.5). Not only are double crossovers less frequent the shorter the distance involved, but it was found that a crossover resulting from an exchange of chromosomes actually prevented another such exchange from occurring in the immediate vicinity. This interference results in no double crossovers if the total distance involved is small.

In subsequent experiments, the relative distances between genes were determined using genes fairly close together. In this way the chromosomes of many organisms have been mapped. It is important to realize that these are relative distances measured by the percentage of crossing over and are given in crossover units (*c.o.*), not in inches or millimeters or thousandths of inches. In the case of *Drosophila,* detailed maps have been worked out for all the chromosomes involving hundreds of *loci* or gene locations. This is also true for other organisms such as corn, *Neurospora* (a pink bread mold) and tomatoes, in which many genes are known and the number of chromosomes is small.

The mapping experiments, including the conclusion of the linear arrangement of genes, give added support to the idea that genes are on chromosomes which are observed to be linear. As we have seen before, however, when a situation seems to be well worked out, there are exceptions to explain and questions to answer. In the usual situation of sex link-age, if a female carrying a recessive sex-linked trait is mated with a male having the dominant trait (see 2a in Fig. 3-1), normally all the sons show the recessive trait (receiving their

X from their mother) but none of the daughters do. Occasionally one daughter may have the trait or one son may not. This occurs in such crosses about once out of two to three thousand offspring. Calvin Bridges, in 1916, suggested an explanation: that throughout meiosis the two **X** chromosomes stay together. If such *non-disjunction* occurs, an egg would result having either two **X** chromosomes or none at all. The egg would then be fertilized by an **X** or a **Y** sperm. Bridges used the mutant trait vermilion eyes (v) which is recessive to normal eye-color. It is linked to the white-eye gene discussed above but is not an allele of it. In this situation four chromosomal situations can arise as a result of fertilization:

Abnormal eggs (chromosome and v genes)				sperm	
XX	or	no **X**		**X**	or **Y**
vv	or	no v		v	no v

	Possible offspring		
XXX	**XXY**	**X**	**Y**
vvv	vv	v	

The first and last zygotes do not survive. The second type would be vermilion-eyed females like their mother and the third group would be red-eyed males like their father. If this explanation is correct, direct examination of the chromosomes should show the females to have two **X**'s and a **Y** chromosome and the males should have one **X** and no **Y**. Rather than wait to observe the very occasional exception, Bridges took such vermilion-eyed females that were fertile (the occasional normal-eyed males were sterile) and mated them to normal males. This makes the situation somewhat more complex but allows many more organisms to work with. If such females are **XXY,** then they can form four types of eggs: **X**(v), **XY**(v), **XX**(vv) and **Y**(no v). Each type can be fertilized either by an **X**(V) or a **Y** sperm. The possible results are:

Eggs	Sperm	Possible Offspring
X(v)	**X**(V)	**XX**(Vv) red-eyed females
XY(v)	**Y**	**XYX**(Vv) red-eyed females
XX(vv)		**XXX** (Vvv) do not survive
Y		**XY**(V) red-eyed males
		XY(v) vermilion-eyed males
		XYY(v) vermilion-eyed males
		XXY(vv) vermilion-eyed females
		YY do not survive

Note that among the possible offspring all vermilion females should have two **X**'s and a **Y**. Whenever the chromosomes of such females were examined, there were nine chromosomes, two being **X**'s and one a **Y**.

Another exception to the usual results in sex linkage took several years to explain. One sex-linked characteristic in *Drosophila* is the occurrence of notches in the wing. Unlike the sex-linked mutants discussed previously, this trait is dominant in the females, and males with the gene die. In addition, if females with the notched wing and normal red eyes (**NW**) are mated with normal winged white-eyed males (**nw**), the female offspring that have notched wings are also white-eyed. Finally, if genes on each side of the notch are mapped, the frequency of crossing over is about 3.8% less than if no notched flies were involved. The final explanation of these strange results is an imaginative but simple one, again supported by direct observation. If a piece of the **X** chromosome were missing, including the place where the **w** gene is usually located, and if this *deletion* causing the phenotype notch were about 3.8 crossover units long, the above results would be expected. There would be no notch males, for too many genes would be totally missing for life to be possible. In the cross between notched females and white-eyed males, the notched females would have one normal chromosome with the normal red-eyed gene and an **X** chromosome with the deletion. Actually this latter chromosome would have neither a gene for white-eye nor its normal allele. The female offspring that were notched again would have the deletion chromosome from their mother and an **X** chromosome from their father carrying the white allele. Since for this one allele they essentially would be hemizygous, they would have white eyes (see Fig. 3-3).

In usual chromosomes, a change such as a small section of a chromosome missing would not be discernible. The discovery of the giant chromosomes in the salivary gland cells became very useful in this situation. When the eggs of flies develop, they first form larvae or maggots. These small white, worm-like forms have tiny black jaws. If these are grasped with tweezers and pulled quickly and firmly, the two salivary glands also are removed quickly and easily. These can be squashed on a slide to break the cells and release the chromosomes. The material is then stained and the large chromosomes can be seen quite easily under a microscope (Fig. 3-4). Each chromosome is seen as a series of dark and light bands, the shape and banding pattern of each chromosome being distinct and specific. Each chromosome is actually the result of many divisions of a pair of synapsed chromosomes, an unusual case of homologous chromosomes pairing, point for point, in cells not undergoing meiosis. When a deletion is present in one of the chromosomes, this precise pairing cannot occur in the area of the deletion and the chromosome not having the deletion buckles (Fig. 3-5).

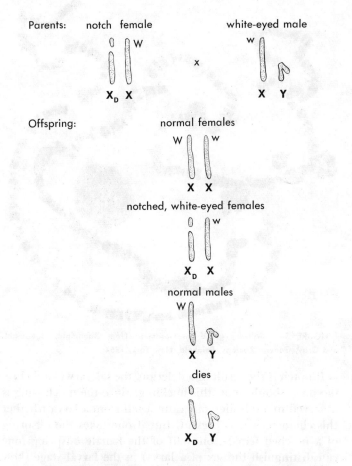

FIGURE 3-3. The deficiency, notch. W = normal eye color, w = white eye, X = normal X chromosome, X_D = X chromosome with deletion resulting in notch wing, Y = Y chromosome.

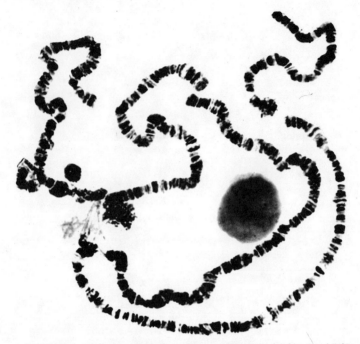

FIGURE 3-4. Salivary gland chromosomes. (From Goodnight, Goodnight, and Gray, *General Zoology*, Reinhold, New York, 1964.)

If notch is the result of a deletion, the salivary gland chromosomes should show this buckling. Since the notch wing is observed in adult flies, one cannot tell from a larva whether this characteristic is present. But if one takes the offspring of a notched female, one-half of the female offspring (one can distinguish the sex of a larva) in the larval stage show this buckling effect in the **X** chromosome of the salivary gland cells.

More and more data accumulated again and again supported the existence of real entities, the genes, located on

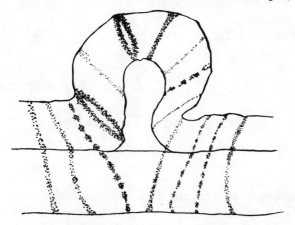

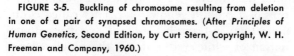

FIGURE 3-5. Buckling of chromosome resulting from deletion in one of a pair of synapsed chromosomes. (After *Principles of Human Genetics,* Second Edition, by Curt Stern, Copyright, W. H. Freeman and Company, 1960.)

chromosomes. Many times the data and their interpretation not only added support to this idea but opened up new avenues of research. Thus the research on deletions allowed another means for precise location of genes, first supplied by the discovery and use of linkage and mapping experiments, making the fruitfly even more appropriate for genetic studies.

chapter four

More Than Two Alleles

Whenever a new mutant fly is discovered, a stock of such flies is established as a source for study. In one such stock, a year after the discovery of white eye, a fly was found which had eyes of a pinkish yellow color, later called eosin. This was more than just another mutant, for it was found in a population of white-eyed and not the usual red-eyed animals. The possibility that it came from outside the stock bottle was eliminated. In addition to white eyes the animals in this bottle also had short wings and black bodies. The new eosin fly also possessed short wings and a black body, neither of which is typical of "normal" or wild-type animals. The conclusion is that the eosin eye, an inherited trait, was the result of a change in one of the white-eyed flies. Previously, mutants had been found in groups of flies with wild-type characteristics. This occurrence of a change in white eye is significant in relation to the idea of a recessive trait being the result of an absence of a specific gene rather than a change from one state to another. White eye is the result of recessive genes. On the basis of the absence hypothesis, it is difficult to imagine the source of the eosin eye, which would require nothing becoming something. One might, however, suggest that another factor, unrelated to white eyes, had changed and covered up the presence of the still present white factors.

With the discovery of any new trait before any such decisions are or can be made, the sensible procedure is to conduct breeding experiments in order to learn about its pattern of inheritance. The white-eyed trait had been found to be due to a sex-linked factor recessive to the wild-type red eye color. When similar crosses involving the new eosin eye color and red eyes were made, exactly comparable results were obtained: eosin was the result of a sex-linked recessive factor. A third eye color, vermilion, also is sex-linked and recessive to wild-type. The question now raised is: "What relationship is there among these three eye colors, white, eosin and vermilion?" One simple possibility is that the genes causing such traits are linked to each other, all being on the **X** chromosome but otherwise not related. The answer comes when various matings are made.

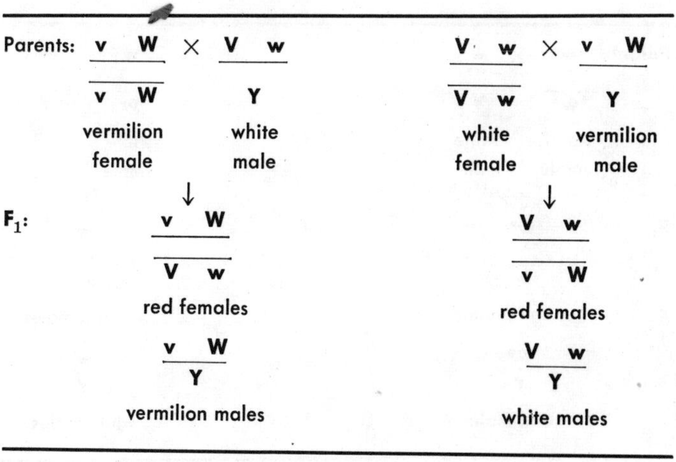

FIGURE 4-1. Crosses involving sex-linked non-alleles.

When vermilion-eyed females are crossed with white-eyed males, the results are red-eyed (wild-type) females and vermilion males (see Fig. 4-1). This is what would be expected if the genes for white and vermilion were non-alleles although sex-linked, the females being like neither parent and the males like the female parent. Furthermore, when these F_1 females, heterozygous for both traits, are test-crossed, typical results of mostly non-crossovers and some crossovers including wild-type males occur, again indicating linkage of these two factors.

Interesting and unusual offspring result when eosin and white-eyed flies are mated. If an eosin female is crossed with a white-eyed male, all the offspring have eosin-colored eyes, although somewhat lighter than the female parent. In the reciprocal cross of white-eyed females and eosin-eyed males, all the female offspring are similarly eosin-eyed and all the males are white-eyed (see Fig. 4-2). In neither case are there

Parents: $\dfrac{w^e}{w^e}$ $\times$ $\dfrac{w}{Y}$ $\dfrac{w}{w}$ $\times$ $\dfrac{w^e}{Y}$

eosin   white   white   eosin
female   male   female   male

$\downarrow$ $\downarrow$

F_1: $\dfrac{w^e}{w}$ $\dfrac{w}{w^e}$

eosin females   eosin females

$\dfrac{w^e}{Y}$ $\dfrac{w}{Y}$

eosin males   white males

FIGURE 4-2. Crosses involving sex-linked alleles.

any wild-type offspring. These are the same types of results by which each of these traits was found to be due to sex-linked, recessive alleles of the factor for red eyes—all offspring like one of the parents, the males being like the mother. The conclusion can be drawn that genes causing eosin and white eyes are alleles of each other, with eosin dominant to white. If each of these factors also is allelic to a gene resulting in red eyes and both recessive to it, then there are three alleles. This conclusion is supported further in that, given the appropriate crosses, no crossovers are found between eosin and white. In other words, there is complete segregation between these two factors indicating that each occupies the same locus on homologous chromosomes. Finally when each factor, eosin and white, is test-crossed with a known linked gene, the same crossover distance is obtained.

A year after the discovery of eosin, a cherry-eyed fly was found. This condition also was found to be a sex-linked characteristic due to a fourth allele of the so-called white locus. At least 15 alleles are now known at this position on the X-chromosome, resulting in various amounts of pigment (see Fig. 4-3). In each case wild-type is dominant but there is lack of dominance shown in females heterozygous for any other two alleles, these heterozygotes being intermediate in phenotype. Note that any male can possess only one allele at a time, and a female can have no more than two different alleles. Only in a mixed population of flies can more than two alleles and three phenotypes be present.

Similar cases of multiple alleles have been demonstrated in a great variety of plants and animals. One of the best and longest known cases of multiple alleles is found in man, the ABO blood groups. Here the initial discovery was of the phenotypes that were not of genetic interest at first. During

Phenotype	Symbol of Allele	Phenotype	Symbol of Allele
Wild type (red)	$+$ or w^+	Honey	w^h
Coral	w^{co}	Buff	w^f
Blood	w^{bl}	Tinged	w^t
Eosin	w^e	Pearl	w^p
Cherry	w^{ch}	Ivory	w^i
Apricot	w^a	White	w

FIGURE 4-3. Alleles at the white locus in *Drosophila melanogaster*.

NOTE: It is customary to use a small letter for a recessive gene and the same base letter with superscripts for a series of alleles.

World War I, Karl Landsteiner discovered that humans could be divided into four groups named **A, B, AB,** and **O,** depending upon characteristics of their red blood cells. The cells of an individual might have one chemical or antigen, **A,** or another, **B.** Some individuals have both antigens, **AB,** or neither, **O.** He also discovered that the non-cellular part of the blood, or serum, also might be characterized by the presence or absence of a chemical antibody. Thus persons who have antigen **A** have a serum substance, antibody **b,** which clumps cells having antigen **B.** Conversely, the serum of **B** individuals has a chemical, antibody **a,** which clumps **A** type cells. **O** persons have both antibodies and **AB** persons have neither. Thus all humans can be classified as to the presence or absence of these antigens and antibodies (see Fig. 4-4). This classification became important, particularly during war time, for blood transfusions can result in serious illness and even death if the wrong combination is made. It is best to supply the same type of blood.

As a result of the importance of these characteristics, many individuals have been blood-typed and large amounts of data have been collected allowing a genetic analysis to be made. Also important to the geneticist is the fact that the

Type	Antigen (red blood cells)	Antibody (serum)	Genotypes
A	A	anti-b	$I^A I^A$ or $I^A i$
B	B	anti-a	$I^B I^B$ or $I^B i$
AB	A and B	none	I^A I^B
O	none	anti-a and anti-b	i i

FIGURE 4-4. The ABO blood groups of man.

antigenic phenotype is present at birth and does not change. Here we can see the methods of determining the inheritance of a trait when controlled breeding experiments are not feasible but much family data are available. Although individual families are small, one can group families and so consolidate the information (see Fig. 4-5). In some cases the type of offspring may vary from family to family. For example, when one parent is A and one parent O, some families show only A-type children; in other families some children may be A and some O. In small individual families all the children might be O type, although in grouping families and in large families the first two cases prevail. When any two O individuals have children, all of them also are O type regardless of the size of the family; but an O individual need not have two O parents. This indicates that O is the recessive state in respect to the A phenotype. Similar data indicate that O is the result of an allele recessive to the factor resulting in type B. The two genes resulting in phenotypes A and B show no dominance or recessiveness with respect to each other since A and B parents may have AB children. There can be four phenotypes and six genotypes in a population of humans as a result of this set of three multiple alleles (see Fig. 4-4).

Parents	Children
O × **O**	all **O**
A × **O**	all **A** or about 1/2 **A** and 1/2 **O**. Small families might have all **O**.
B × **O**	all **B** or about 1/2 **B** and 1/2 **O**. Small families might have all **O**.
AB × **O**	about 1/2 **A** and 1/2 **B**. Small families might be all **A** or all **B**.
A × **A**	all **A** or about 3/4 **A**, 1/4 **O**. Small families might have all **O**.
B × **B**	all **B** or about 3/4 **B**, 1/4 **O**. Small families might have all **O**.
A × **AB**	Some families **A** and **AB**; others **AB**, **A**, and **B**. Small families might be all **A**, **B**, or **AB** but no **O**.
B × **AB**	Some families **B** and **AB**; others **AB**, **A**, and **B**. Small families might be all **A**, **B**, or **AB** but no **O**.
A × **B**	all types.

FIGURE 4-5. Family data of ABO blood groups.

Since the discovery of these blood types, many other blood antigens in man and other mammals have been discovered. The Rh factor is such an antigen. Again a series of classifications can be made and the results indicate a series of at least eight multiple alleles not related to those resulting in the ABO blood groups. One physiologically important difference in this case is that antibodies against an antigen are not naturally present in persons who are Rh-negative and do not possess that antigen. If such a person, however, receives a transfusion of that antigen, he will develop antibodies to it. If such a woman has an Rh-positive child as a result of the father being Rh-positive, the mother *may* develop antibodies against the Rh antigen. These antibodies *may* get across the placenta and *may* clump the cells of the child enough to result in a so-called Rh baby or a child with erythroblastosis foetalis. These antibodies can be detected in the mother's serum and proper preparations can be made for the care of the child.

These are only a few examples of many phenotypes that result from a series of three or more alleles. A fairly clear picture emerges—that of a particulate unit of several alternative forms occupying a specific location on a specific chromosome, and affecting the same characteristic. The ultimate test of alleles versus linked non-alleles is that the former show no crossing over, as linked genes do, but always complete segregation. Until the late 40's and early 50's, this seemed to complete this area of study other than finding more and more examples of multiple alleles. The discovery of *pseudoalleles* again forced geneticists to reconsider their concept of the gene.

Whenever a mutant of *Drosophila* was discovered, a stock culture was set up even though the particular mutant previously may have been found and a stock established. In this way many allelic series and duplication of alleles were available by the late 40's. The same mutants were given different superscripts to indicate a different source. Lozenge (lz) eye is a mutant characteristic of fruitflies, the eyes being narrow, oval-shaped with rough and smooth areas, actually giving the effect of a lozenge. When two such mutants, lz^g and lz^{BS}, were crossed, all offspring were expected to have lozenge eyes, the adults being $lz^{BS}lz^g$ comparable to the F_1 heterozygotes in Fig. 4-2. Furthermore, crossing of such lozenge F_1

flies should also yield only lozenge flies. Surprisingly, a few normal red-eyed flies were found. If this cross actually involved two closely linked genes, these normal flies would be the result of crossing over (see Fig. 4-6). By using "marker genes" known to be located near the lozenge locus, the possibility of spontaneous mutation was ruled out. For example, if one had $\frac{a\ lz^{BS}\ +\ b}{+\ +\ lz^{g}\ +}$ (phenotypically being lozenge), then a crossover between lz^{BS} and lz^{g} loci would result in the gametes $\underline{a\ lz^{BS}\ lz^{g}+}$ and $\underline{+\ +\ +\ b}$. If the latter gamete were fertilized by an $\underline{a\ lz^{BS}\ +\ b}$ gamete, its phenotype would be b, the eyes being red. The presence of the b phenotype would indicate a crossover rather than a mutation.

These genes are called pseudoalleles because they seem to result in the same phenotype; and unless many offspring of the proper mating are observed, the results are typical of multiple alleles. In the case of the lozenge phenotype, three closely linked loci were demonstrated. In one case involving

---

Parents: (lozenge) $\frac{lz^{BS}\quad +}{+\quad lz^{g}} \times \frac{lz^{BS}\quad +}{+\quad lz^{g}}$ (female parent source of crossover)

Offspring: Most are lozenge: $\frac{lz^{BS}\quad +}{+\quad lz^{g}}$ $\frac{lz^{BS}\quad +}{lz^{BS}\quad +}$ $\frac{+\quad lz^{g}}{+\quad lz^{g}}$

A few rare crossovers including: $\frac{+\quad +}{lz^{BS}\quad +}$ $\frac{+\quad +}{+\quad lz^{g}}$

both red eyed

FIGURE 4-6. Cross of two lozenge pseudoalleles. + = allele for normal phenotype.

vermilion-eyed flies, only two crossovers out of 78,934 offspring were observed and about 50,000 were counted before the first one was found. By observing such large numbers of offspring from appropriately controlled matings, several examples of pseudoallelism have been discovered. The white locus itself, the first of the multiple alleles, is known to consist of five very closely linked loci. It is quite possible that some genes now considered alleles may be pseudoalleles. This would be particularly likely in organisms such as man or cows in which proper mating is difficult to set up or in which such large numbers of offspring are almost impossible to obtain.

Since these pseudoalleles, such as lozenge, are actually linked genes, different heterozygotes can be obtained. If two lozenge genes are on the same chromosome, i.e. $\dfrac{lz^{BS} \quad lz^{g}}{+ \quad +}$, the flies have normal red eyes. If, however, the lozenge genes are on different homologous chromosomes as in $\dfrac{lz^{BS} \quad +}{+ \quad lz^{g}}$, the flies have lozenge eyes. The position of the mutant genes is the only difference between these two situations. This *position effect* is related not to the transmission of these genes from one generation to the next nor to their chemical nature, but to their physiological functioning dependent upon their physical location.

The existence of pseudoallelic systems presents two problems to the modern geneticist. One is the position effect relating to the action of the genes. The other is a challenge to the whole concept of the gene. So far the gene has been the unit of transmission, the "classical" gene. For the most part it had been assumed that this transmitted gene was equivalent to a physiological unit. Although some pseudoalleles may have subtle differences, their over-all effects and major effects are alike although they may occupy three (lozenge loci) or even five (white loci) positions on chromosomes separable by crossing over. This was one of the first indications that the geneticist might have to consider more than one kind of gene unit.

chapter five

More Than One Set of Genes

Long before the discovery of genetics, plant and animal breeders were able to improve the milk production of cows or the production of rice per acre by controlled breeding procedures. This indicated that these characteristics are at least partially the result of heredity. The same animals or plants varied if the food or climate differed, showing that the environment also played an important role in the final phenotype expressed.

Discrete characteristics such as color, wing shape, and blood groups can be genetically analyzed with relative ease. Quantitative qualities including height and weight and showing continuous variation present a much more difficult problem. E. M. East was one of the first geneticists to attempt a careful study of the inheritance of such traits. Working with tobacco, *Nicotiana,* he first raised many species under a great variety of environmental conditions, carefully measuring many characteristics such as height, size of leaves, and length of corolla or petals. In the latter case he made an interesting observation. In a given species, regardless of the conditions of growth, the petal (corolla) length showed relatively little variation. For example, one species, when grown in small pots, had no leaves larger than seven inches and when grown in the field, had 30 inch leaves; yet in both cases the petals were about the same size. East then picked two groups of plants each showing relative constancy of petal size but differing markedly from each other. Using these two types, he obtained F_1 and F_2 generations. He presented some of his problems in 1913: *

This then seemed to be an excellent opportunity for studying size inheritance: two strains, uniform in pure lines, one with a corolla three times the length of the other, could be crossed easily. All was not plain sailing, however, for the plants of the F_1 generation were absolutely self sterile. This fact would have cut off the experiment in the flower of a promising youth but for the further fact that each plant was perfectly cross-fertile with every other plant. It did indeed reduce my interest in the inheritance of corolla size, for it precluded the study of an F_3 generation, but this was offset by the more fascinating problem of sterility.

Later, East did study self-sterility although he doesn't mention it again in this paper. He proceeds in reporting his results having measured the petal size of all the F_1 and F_2 plants that he raised. (see Fig. 5-1)

At first glance, this table may seem a confusing mass of numbers. In the first place, he had obtained petals of a great variety of sizes. In order to be able to report his data in an organized manner, he classified the petals' sizes within a range. Thus, petals between 23 and 27 mm in length are in the 25-mm category. This is the data East had to work with and it is worth careful study. Some generalizations can be noted. First, the parents are of two extremes, short and long. For example, there are a total of 170 plants of the "short" parent, 9 having petals in the 20-mm category, 133 in the 25-mm class and 28 plants in the 30-mm group. In contrast, the shortest of the "long" parents had petals in the 65-mm

* *Botanical Gazette,* vol. LV, 1913.

FREQUENCY DISTRIBUTION

Source of Petals	Nearest Length in Millimeters	Number of Plants														
		20	25	30	35	40	45	50	55	60	65	70	75	80	85	90
Parent #1		9	133	28												
Parent #2											1	19	50	56	32	9
F_1					3	30	58	20								
F_2			5	27	79	136	125	132	102	105	64	30	15	6	2	

STATISTICAL CONSTANTS

	Mean	Standard Deviation
Parent #1	25.6	2.27
Parent #2	78.8	5.34
F_1	44.3	3.67
F_2	49.9	11.26

FIGURE 5-1. Frequency distribution and statistical constants of petal length in tobacco. (Modified from East, *Botanical Gazette*, Vol. LV, 1913. Permission of University of Chicago Press.)

category. Secondly, the F_1 plants show sizes between the parents and no extreme members. Finally, the F_2 offspring show all sizes, including petals like both parents and like the F_1.

It would be helpful to be able to be more precise about these results. By averaging the petal size for each generation it is found that the mean (average) petal length of the parents is 25.6 mm and 78.8 mm. The F_1 and F_2 means are 44.3 mm and 49.9 mm, respectively. This clearly and in much less space shows the extreme differences between the original parents, and that the F_1 offspring are intermediate between the parents. But it in no way indicates that the F_2 petals are of all sizes and that the range of the F_1 is small.

There are calculations that will show these facts. For example, the *standard deviation* represents the degree to which members in each generation differ from the average of that group. In this case the standard deviations of the parents are 2.27 and 5.38, indicating that the "long" parent population showed more variation. The one parental group having an average petal length of 25.6 had petals ranging from 20 to 30 mm, whereas the other parent with an average length of 78.8 had petal lengths from 65 to 90 mm. The one varied only by 10 mm, the other by 25 mm. The F_1 and F_2 standard deviations are 3.67 and 11.26. From these numbers one can conclude that the F_2 had the greatest spread or variation from the average and that the F_1 plants showed less variation than one parent. The standard deviation, however, does not show the actual differences in size, so that both mean and standard deviations are valuable calculations.

In many similar experiments this same pattern emerged: parental inbred strains widely different from each other when mated yield offspring with relatively little variation and measurements intermediate between the parents. These offspring, in turn, have offspring that show great variation. Sometimes, although not always, some F_2 individuals will be as extreme as the original parents. But what can be concluded about the specific inheritance of such traits?

The simplest approach is to use genetic knowledge already available. When two individuals homozygous for two pairs of genes involved in the development of two different traits are mated (**AABB** × **aabb** or **AAbb** × **aaBB**), the expected results are clear. The F_1 are all heterozygous (**AaBb**) and alike. If two such F_1 individuals are crossed, the F_2 show all combinations with about $1/16$ $(1/4)^2$ being like one of the original parents and $1/16$ like the other parent. Similarly when three non-linked pairs of alleles are studied in the same way, $1/64$ $(1/4)^3$ have the phenotype of one of the parents.

Instead of three sets of alleles involving different traits, one might assume several pairs of non-linked alleles all affecting the *same* trait, one of each of these (the effective allele) adding to a particular dimension. Lack of dominance is also assumed, that **AA** is twice as effective as **Aa**. Finally, as a working hypothesis, each effective allele is considered to have an equal effect so that **AAbb** would have the same action as **AaBb** and **AABB** would add twice as much to the phenotype as the first two genotypes. Such a scheme can be applied in analyzing the data of East.

Through several generations of self-fertilization each original strain of tobacco used by East may be assumed to be homozygous. The genotypes of the short parent (#1) can be designated as **aabbcc.......n** and of the long parent (#2) as **AABBCC.......n**. Capital letters are used to denote the effective genes adding to petal length when present. If two such plants are crossed, the F_1 is **AaBbCc.......n**. Being genetically alike, they should be alike phenotypically.

Having fewer effective genes than parent #2 and more than parent #1, the petal length should be intermediate between the two parents. If such F_1 plants are mated, the F_2 should show all possible phenotypes, and so the standard deviation should be high. A specific proportion should be like the parental types, depending upon the number of gene pairs involved in the inheritance of petal length. Applying these conclusions to the tobacco data, we find some agreement and some discrepancies.

First, the parents and F_1 are not uniform, although the standard deviation is low. This can be accounted for in two ways. The most obvious explanation is that the environment is not uniform from plant to plant so that, although the genotypes are the same, the phenotypic expressions vary within a relatively narrow range. The second possibility is that, in spite of inbreeding, the parent plants are not uniform genotypically. Since the original plants were the result of several generations of self-fertilization, this explanation is unlikely.

The F_1 petals, although not alike, are intermediate between the petal lengths of the parents. The F_2 does show the expected wide range of variation but it is not so easy to estimate the number of genes involved. There are 828 F_2 plants. If there were two pairs of genes involved, we would expect 1/16 of them or 51.75 plants to have petals like the short parent and 51.75 like the long parent (see Fig. 5-2). Obviously this figure must be rounded off, since there are only whole plants. The number of smallest and largest F_2 plants are not this frequent. Not so obvious is what number in the F_2 distribution is to be used because of variation among the parental plants.

For example, the short parent ranges from 20 to 30 mm. None of the F_2 is as short as 20, 5 are in the 25-mm range

Number of gene pairs involved (n)	Proportion of F_2 expected to be like parent $(1/4)^n$	Number out of 828 F_2 plants expected to be like parent $(1/4)^n \times 828$
2	1/16	51.75
3	1/64	12.93
4	1/256	3.23
5	1/1024	less than 1 (.81)

FIGURE 5-2. Number of F_2 individuals expected to be like parental types based on the number of gene pairs involved.

and 27 are as long as 30 mm. Should one assume no F_2's are like the parent since none is 20 mm long; or should one use 5 as the significant number; or 32 as the total number of F_2 plants that resemble the parent? On the first basis, one would estimate 5 or more pairs of genes involved; the second number would result in an estimate of 4 pairs, and the last number would indicate 2 or 3 pairs. The choice is not clear. The fact that no F_2 plants are as short or long as the shortest and longest parents cannot be altered. All that is indicated is that more F_2 plants should be obtained, particularly if 5 or more pairs of genes are suspected. Since the F_2 plants are of all types, the 27 plants in the 30-mm category do not necessarily include plants only like the short parent genotypically. Plants that have a genetic potential of 35 or even 40 mm might be in this category because of environmental effects. On this basis, East used the five 25 mm F_2 plants in estimating the number of gene pairs as 4.

The long F_2 plants should show the same estimate. But these plants also present problems. Again none is like the longest of the long parent and there is much greater variation among the long parent plants. Many more F_2 plants are like them also. East attempted an explanation and correction for this relatively high standard deviation of the long parent population. The classes of categories used are chosen by the investigator. Thus East might have classified his petals in groups of 1 mm difference rather than ranges of 5 mm. Also, the range of all groups need not be the same. East decided that the longer a flower was, the greater was the absolute effect of environmental conditions. For example, soil conditions might decrease the potential petal length by 20%. A petal capable of being 30 mm would then be 6 mm shorter, or 24 mm, and be placed in the 25-mm category. In contrast, a potentially 80-mm petal reduced 20% would be 64 mm in length and in a much lower category. To correct for this type of error, East, using exactly the same data, regrouped his material so that as the length increased the range of a particular class also was increased. When this is done, the distribution of the long parent and the similar F_2 plants is given in Fig. 5-3.

Class Range: (mm)	46–53 8	54–62 9	63–72 10	73–83 11	84–95 12
Parent #2	0	0	20	106	41
F_2	210	189	94	23	2

FIGURE 5-3. Partial reclassification of data of East.

Now there are two F_2 plants in the highest category of the long parent. On this basis there is agreement with the conclusion reached using the short F_2 individuals. Four pairs of genes are involved in the inheritance of petal length in tobacco. Actually, East continued this work. He raised more F_2 plants, including some obviously like the extreme parents, and revised his estimate to 5 or more pairs of genes involved.

There are obvious difficulties with this working hypothesis

concerning the polygenic inheritance of quantitative traits. First, it is assumed that none of the genes are linked, limiting the maximum number of gene pairs to the number of chromosome pairs in a particular species. If this were true, then no characteristic of corn, much used in this type of study, could be the result of more than 10 pairs of genes, since this is the number of chromosome pairs in corn. Similarly, the limit in *Drosophila melanogaster* would be 4. This limit, of course, is not likely.

It is also unlikely that all the genes involved have equal and cumulative effects. There is no necessity, for instance, that every gene influencing petal length should add precisely 2.5 mm to the potential length of the petal. In man it is easy to imagine many genes influencing the final height of the individual by affecting such things as length of neck, length of shin bone, or curvature of the spine. It is difficult, however, to reason that their effects are equal.

There are two possibilities in dealing with such difficulties. One is to know and accept the limitations of such a hypothesis, and to use it when it is workable. This has often been done. In the inheritance of skin color Davenport in 1913 suggested that Negroes native to central and west Africa differ from white individuals by two pairs of genes showing no dominance, each effective gene adding pigment to the skin. In this scheme white individuals have no effective genes and their genotype can be given as $p_1p_1p_2p_2$. The Negro has four effective genes, $P_1P_1P_2P_2$. Mulattoes resulting from parents of these two types would be $P_1p_1P_2p_2$ and be intermediate in skin color. Children of such mulattoes can be of all types ranging from white to black (see Fig. 5-4). One can also conclude that if one parent is white with no pigment-adding genes to contribute, no children can be darker than the darker parent. It is clear that this hypothesis will

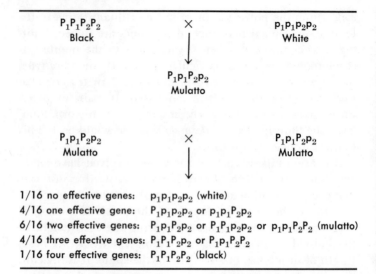

FIGURE 5-4. Hypothesis of two pairs of genes influencing inheritance of skin pigment in humans.

not account for many small variations in degree of pigmentation that occur. Some of these variations may be due to environmental conditions and some may be the result of modifying genes, which might cause a slight increase in the amount or type of pigment produced. It has, however, been a very workable hypothesis when used to analyze the main pigment differences between Negroes and whites.

Another possibility for overcoming the difficulties encountered in studying polygenic inheritance is to develop hypotheses that are more realistic but more difficult to apply. Much more subtle statistical methods of analysis and prediction are needed if one assumes linkage and unequal effect of genes. Statistical methods also have been devised for estimating the relative role of inheritance and environment. These are beyond the scope of this book, but indicate the need for cooperation between statisticians and geneticists.

One useful approach in examining the relative role of environment and heredity is in the study of twins. Of particular value are observations of identical twins, fraternal twins of the same sex, and of separated twins. Presumably twins raised together have had essentially the same environment. Identical twins, resulting from the same egg and sperm, also share the same genetic equipment. Fraternal twins, having the same parents but developing from different eggs and sperm, have genotypes as different as any brothers or sisters. Fraternal twins only of the same sex are studied for two reasons: since identical twins are always of the same sex, this would make the two groups more comparable; and having twins of different sexes would add unnecessary factors.

When identical twins are found to be more like each other than fraternal twins are like each other, this greater degree of likeness is taken as a measure of the role of heredity with respect to the trait or traits being investigated. Also of great value are a few studies made of identical twins reared apart from an early age. Here, in contrast to normal fraternal twins, the genetic heritage is alike but the environments are different. In such investigations there have been differences between twins but also amazing likenesses, including close similarities in I. Q., vocational interests, mental illnesses, etc. One of the main difficulties, however, is that those characteristics of greatest interest, such as "intelligence," "temperament," skills, are the most difficult to define and measure. On the whole, these studies indicate that most characteristics, including intelligence and temperament, have an inherited basis in addition to an environmentally influenced development.

Some generalizations about polygenic inheritance can be made without knowing the specific number or action of the individual genes involved. Inbreeding, i.e., the mating of individuals more closely related to each other than the average parents, results in an increase in the degree of homozygosity so that the individuals are more alike and the standard deviation decreases. The explanation is clear. The more closely two individuals are related, the more likely they are to have genes in common. This increase in homozygosity is not necessarily bad. If the effect of such genes is advantageous or desirable, then such inbreeding is of benefit. This is the basis of much selective breeding in practical agricultural programs.

Very early in the history of genetics, W. Johannsen studied the effect of selection on quantitative traits using weight of bean seeds as the characteristic followed. Essentially he found a limit to the effectiveness of selection. If inbreeding increases homozygosity, once this condition is complete, i.e., all genes involved are homozygous, inbreeding can no longer have an effect. Then one can only improve the results by improving the environmental conditions.

Other difficulties are encountered in inbreeding programs. Recessive genes may be present in one or both parents in the heterozygous condition and so not be expressed in the phenotype. If the trait is desired, the proper parents with the gene may not be identified at first. Once the homozygous individuals are obtained and the gene expressed, the problem is solved. A greater problem is the occurrence of undesirable recessive traits. The homozygous individuals are identifiable and can be weeded out. But there probably are heterozygous individuals carrying the gene but not showing it. Identifying such "carriers" so as not to use them in a mass breeding program is more difficult and time-consuming. Often, if the ancestry is not known, suspected individuals must be used as parents and, if the trait shows up in the offspring, that parent and his offspring must be discarded as future parents. At first this may seem wasteful, but in the long run it is worth the time and effort. When many pairs of genes are involved, parents can be carefully selected as having the desired trait and careful records kept of the performance of the following generations.

Another problem of inbreeding is that, in order to increase the number of effective genes involved in a desired trait, one may also increase the homozygosity of genes resulting in an undesired trait. For example, one may increase the amount of wheat per acre but also concentrate genes which increase the sensitivity of the wheat to infection by a fungus. What is often done is to develop high grain-producing plants and other highly resistant plants through inbreeding. Then the two inbred plants are "out-crossed" and further selective inbreeding continued in order to combine different advantageous traits.

In such inbreeding and outbreeding procedures an interesting phenomenon was discovered. In some cases, including corn, when plants were inbred over a few generations they became less vigorous. Admittedly this is a vague term, for the effect is a general one in terms of number of kernels, size of plant, straightness of rows of kernels and general health. When two such inbred lines are crossed, the hybrids are very healthy, showing *hybrid vigor,* also called *heterosis.* This is the basis of the hybrid corn in common use today. In this case four inbred lines of corn are used. None of them resembles the large ears of corn with regular rows of succulent kernels sold on the market. Of the four inbred strains (**A, B, C, D**), two are crossed with each other (**A** × **B** and **C** × **D**) and then the two hybrids are crossed, resulting in marketable corn. This must be repeated each time, for if these hybrid corns are mated to each other, the offspring show great variation, including many undesirable characteristics.

Why should concentrated inbreeding lead to a loss of vigor and out-crossing of inbred lines lead to greatly increased vigor? A completely satisfactory explanation is still to come. One hypothesis is that "vigor" is the result of many growth factors. These growth factors are in turn the result of many dominant genes, the heterozygote contributing as much as the homozygous dominant. When an organism is inbred, homozygosity of both dominant and recessive genes is increased. The dominant ones will give some added growth to the organisms. But many of the dominant genes present in the originally heterozygous individuals will be replaced by recessive genes not contributing to the general health of the offspring. In the same way, hybrid vigor is explained on the basis of a sudden large increase in the number of such dominant genes. One inbred parent may be **AABBCCddeeff** and the other parent **aabbccDDEEFF,** each having three different growth factor genes. The hybrid would be **AaBbCdDdEeFf,** having six different growth factor genes. This also helps explain why organisms homozygous for all these genes cannot be obtained by careful inbreeding; if this were the case, one could have an inbred pure strain showing hybrid vigor. If many genes are involved, the chance of getting **AABBCCDDEEFF** individuals in an F_2 is slim $(1/4)^6$. Also, if many genes are involved, linkage must be considered. If two of the genes are in the following positions **A b/a B,** getting an **AABB** individual depends upon the frequency of crossing over, which further reduces the possibility of developing such strains.

Some geneticists believe this still does not explain the

great and striking increase in vigor shown by hybrids and the inability to obtain inbred strains with equal vigor. They have suggested that an **Aa** individual has a greater gene activity than an **AA** individual and that such *over-dominance* is the reason for the general improvement.

These many questions to be answered in the field of quantitative genetics make it one of the most intriguing areas of study for both geneticists and statisticians. Many of these problems involve those traits of greatest interest to man. Cooperation with psychologists in terms of defining and measuring many of these characteristics also is needed. In spite of these open questions, this is the area used to the greatest advantage in applied genetics in developing domestic plants and animals.

chapter six

Genes Can Change

By the 1920's, many variations of phenotype in a large number of organisms had been discovered and studied in relation to their patterns of inheritance. Often these variations found to be inherited occurred suddenly in controlled, inbred populations, leading to the conclusion that genes can change. Once such a mutation has occurred, the "new" gene with a few exceptions is as stable and unchanging as its previous form. In addition to studying the patterns of transmission of these genes, the questions of how and why genes mutate became a special area of study by geneticists.

The first question that may come to mind is: "How often do such changes occur?" Although this may seem a simple question to answer, it presents several difficulties. To be answered accurately, a question must be asked in a very specific form. Should one consider how often a particular gene changes to a particular form? Or how often it changes in any way? Or how often any of the genes of an individual change? Or how often any of the genes of a population of individuals change? Even after deciding what change is to be measured, the meaning of "how often" is still to be tackled. Obviously this means some kind of time unit, but the choice is an important one. It might be hours or years. But what is hours for one organism is equivalent to years for another. To be able to compare results in different organisms it is essential to have comparable units. One possibility is generation time, that is, the time it takes for one generation of individuals to produce the next generation. A bacterial generation may be 20 minutes, a fruitfly generation 10–14 days, and a human generation is considered to be 25 years. Obviously this is an average estimate; a human doesn't take 25 years to produce the next generation, but the average difference in age between parents and offspring is 25 years. This, too, being an average and representing populations, presents difficulties in determining mutations found in so many gametes. Thus a gamete is a specific unit, egg or sperm, but it also represents generation time as it is the link between generations.

It was clear from the beginning that changes of a particular gene are very rare whatever the unit of time used. The rate of change from the normal allele to the gene, **w**, resulting in white eye in *Drosophila* is about 1 mutation in 30,000 gametes or a rate of 0.3/10,000 gametes. One estimate for the rate of mutation of the gene resulting in hemophilia is 32 mutations per one million gametes or also 0.3/10,000 gametes. Some genes are known to have a relatively high mutation rate. Thus one gene in corn is estimated to have a mutation rate of 18 out of 10,000 gametes. Regardless of the estimate given, it is also clear that to wait for a specific mutation to occur would not be a very profitable way of investigating this problem.

One of the first approaches in studying rates of mutation illustrates the importance of the design of an experiment, utilizing the imagination in applying known genetic facts to discover specific information. This experiment developed by H. J. Muller in the 1920's is known as the ClB method.

One group of genes known as lethal genes is observable

only by the fact that their presence in some way results in the death of the organism possessing them. These may be recessive or dominant genes. In the case of sex-linked recessive lethal genes, a heterozygous female (Ll) would survive, but any male possessing such a gene on his **X** chromosome (lY) would die. Two other genetic factors also were utilized. A dominant sex-linked gene (B) results in a bar-shaped eye in any fly possessing it. Finally, it was found that if a piece of a chromosome were inverted, crossing over was prevented or inhibited in that chromosome. One such inversion was known as the C inversion present in the **X** chromosome and preventing crossing over.

Muller put these three things together using a female heterozygous for a sex-linked recessive lethal, for the Bar gene and for the C inversion. Such a female may be represented as $\underline{C\ \ l\ \ B}$. The only visible difference from a normal fly would be the appearance of a bar-shaped eye. He crossed each such female with a normal male with the following results:

	Females		Males	
Parents:				
Genotype of **X** chromosome:	$\underline{C\ \ l\ \ B}$	$\times$	$\overline{Y}$	
Phenotype:	Bar-eye		Normal	
Offspring:				
Genotype of **X** chromosome:	$\underline{C\ \ l\ \ B}$	$\underline{}$	$\dfrac{C\ \ l\ \ B}{Y}$	$\dfrac{}{Y}$
Phenotype:	Bar-eye	Normal	Dies	Normal

The sex-ratio obtained is 2/3 females and 1/3 males, one-half of the potential males possessing the sex-linked lethal gene and dying. The purpose of this first cross is to obtain females in which the sources of her two **X** chromosomes is known and each is identifiable. Thus all the Bar female offspring above have two **X** chromosomes, the one with the B gene from their mother, the other from their father. In addition, in the formation of her gametes, the C inversion will prevent any exchange between these two **X** chromosomes. Each of the Bar female offspring is allowed to mate with her normal brothers and then removed and her offspring observed. This cross may be represented as $\dfrac{\text{C} \quad \text{l} \quad \text{B}}{\text{---} \quad \text{--} \quad \text{---} \quad \text{--}}$

Bar female $\times$ $\dfrac{}{\text{Y}}$ male. Ordinarily the offspring possible are the same as described in the first cross: 1/3 Bar females, 1/3 normal females and 1/3 normal males, the ClB/Y males dying. If, however, in the gametes formed by the original male parent of the first cross, a mutation to a sex-linked lethal occurred, the female used in the second cross would then have a lethal gene on each **X** chromosome: $\dfrac{\text{C} \quad \text{l} \quad \text{B}}{\text{---} \quad \text{--} \quad \text{--} \quad \text{--} \quad l_2}$. These would be non-alleles since she is alive,

but all her sons would die, as they would receive either one lethal gene or the other. Thus the fact that no males are formed is sufficient to identify the occurrence of a lethal sex-linked recessive mutation. This can be done easily without a microscope, and many such observations may be made relatively quickly. Also the normal daughters will carry this mutation so that it can be studied further. Thus the spontaneous mutation rate of a particular group of genes may be measured, as well as the occurrence of lethal sex-linked recessive mutations in the **X** chromosomes of the gametes produced by the original male. This rate was found to be 15 lethals formed per 10,000 X-bearing sperm. In addition, if a non-lethal but visible sex-linked recessive mutation occurs in the X chromosome being tested, all the males formed in the second cross will show this trait. Thus a quick glance at the offspring will reveal normal males and therefore no mutation; or no males and therefore lethal mutation; or abnormal males and therefore a specific non-lethal mutation. Similar experiments were devised by Muller for testing the other chromosomes of *Drosophila*.

As described above, the spontaneous mutation rate can be measured. If each of the original males is treated in some manner, the effect of that treatment upon the rate of mutation may be discovered. In this way, an increase of temperature was found to cause an increase in mutation rate. In 1927 Muller reported that x-irradiation increased the mutation rate for which he received the Nobel prize in 1946. It is clear that it was not x-rays but the design of the experiment that was so significant.

Others previously had reported evidence which suggested this effect of x-rays but only by such carefully planned experiments as that of Muller was definitive evidence of the effect of x-rays upon mutation rate obtained. For example, in one experiment Muller found no mutations occurring in 198 untreated chromosomes but 49 lethals, 4 semi-lethals (a few males surviving) and 1 visible mutation in 676 treated chromosomes.

Further studies of the effect of x-irradiation on mutation rates in fruitflies revealed that the rate of mutation was proportional to the amount of irradiation and irrespective of the length of time during which a particular dose was given. A dose of 4,000 roentgens (a roentgen is a unit of measurement of the intensity of x-rays) results in the same increase in mutation rate whether applied in seconds, hours or days and results in twice the increase caused by 2,000 roentgens. Although tests are difficult and time-consuming, the effect of very low doses of irradiation have been determined and doses as low as 25 roentgens have been shown to increase the mutation rate significantly.

Some chemicals such as mustard gas and related compounds have been found to be mutagenic. These physical phenomena, i.e., x-rays, gamma rays, ultraviolet, and chemicals such as mustard gas and formaldehyde, also increase the rate of structural changes in chromosomes, including non-disjunction, breakage, inversions, loss of parts of chromosomes and exchanges between non-homologous chromosomes. In some cases it is difficult to distinguish between a gene change and a small chromosomal change. Thus all such changes are known as mutations. Whether a gene mutation or a chromosomal mutation is involved should be stated when known.

At first the effect of irradiation on mutation rate was of only theoretical interest. For one thing, it enabled geneticists to produce more mutations to study. Particular mutations could not be produced, but just increasing the general rate was of value. Its relation to organic evolution was very significant and will be discussed briefly in Chapter 8. Since 1945, however, the significance of irradiation for increasing mutation rates has assumed a greater practical meaning. If as a result of radioactive substances, atomic energy, fall-out from nuclear weapons and use of fluoroscopes and x-ray machines man is to be exposed to increasing amounts of radiation, its effect and control become of paramount and personal importance.

The question now becomes what is the genetic effect of irradiation on man? There are two ways to approach this:

to assume that what is found in other organisms directly applies to man or to study the effect on man directly. Each approach has its difficulties and uncertainties.

The data from fruitflies imply that there is no "safe-dose" of radiation, that however low the exposure there will be some effect.

In 1961, Glass and Ritterhoff studied the effect of very low doses. The design of the experiment is relatively simple. Progeny of non-irradiated flies and of flies given 5 roentgens of x-rays were examined for the appearance of specific dominant mutations. The real problems involve the numbers of organisms to be observed. When one says any dose will have an effect, it does not mean every individual gamete is affected, but that given large enough numbers the effect will occur. Over one million flies were counted. In the control group were found 283 mutations or 0.048% and 323 mutants or 0.055% in the treated group—an increase of 0.007%. Is this a real difference or a chance one? In statistical analyses, what one calculates is the probability of something occurring by chance. Obviously if something is liable to occur 75% of the time by chance alone and it does occur, one attributes it to chance. If, however, something is expected to occur randomly only one out of 100 times or 1%, is its occurrence the result of chance or of a specific effect built into the event? Arbitrarily statisticians have agreed at levels of significance of either 1 or 5%. Thus if something occurs and it is expected only 5% of the time by chance, the occurrence or difference between two groups is said to be significant and therefore attributable to the factor varied in the experiment. In this case, the probability of the 0.007% difference in mutation rate is either 5 or 7.6%, depending upon the handling of the data. Using these statistical methods, the conclusion reached is that this difference is significant, although just barely.

Another problem is the relation of this increase in mutation rate of 0.007% to the increase shown by higher doses. Is the effect proportional to amount of irradiation even at such low doses? Using previous results of controls and the effect of 1,000 and 2,000 roentgens, the authors predicted what one might expect at 5 roentgens. The predictions were a spontaneous mutation rate in the controls of 0.04% and an increase of 0.005% in the experimental group. Their results showed higher results both in the control and the amount of increase. They concluded that doses as low as 5 roentgens did increase the mutation rate in fruitflies and that this increase was directly proportional to the increase found with higher doses.

Whether what is found in one organism can be applied directly to an entirely different organism is important. It is accepted from a great variety of sources that in general radiation dosage does increase the mutation rate. Work with mice, however, indicates that the quantitative effects may not be completely comparable. Dr. and Mrs. Russell undertook a study of the effect of irradiation on the mutation rate in mice. Irradiated normal males were crossed with females known to have seven specific recessive traits. They observed the offspring of such matings and of a control group of non-irradiated parents for the presence of any of these traits. The presence would indicate that a mutation had occurred in the gametes of the male parent. Again it was clear that radiation increased the mutation rate, but the increase was not linear with dosage. At 300 roentgens one would expect the increase to be half that at 600 roentgens. The Russells found a higher increase at 300 roentgens than was expected. In addition, they found the rate of mutation at a given dose to be higher than that in *Drosophila*. In another experiment the total dose given was about the same; but in one group the dose was given in a short period as an acute dose and in another group the male parents were subjected to irradiation at low doses for a period of weeks. Their results suggest that the acute exposure had a greater effect on mutation rate than the chronic.

Mice seem to be more sensitive than fruitflies to the genetic effects of irradiation. Does this mean that humans are even more sensitive? As we do not know the reasons for the difference between the fruitflies and the mice, this question cannot be answered. As a result of these data, the committees responsible for establishing standards of limits of exposure to humans have lowered the "safe-dosage," although the true situation in humans is not known.

These experiments suggest that direct knowledge of the effects of radiation on humans would be of great value. This, too, presents very difficult problems. Obviously, humans should not be purposely exposed to irradiation, nor can the choice of parents be controlled, using one parent with specific marker genes, which is the basis for experimental design in other organisms. The approach must be different. Generally researchers have compared the offspring of individuals exposed to radiation above the normal exposure with that of individuals not so exposed. These include children of x-ray technicians, radiologists, patients subject to medical treatment and the survivors of the atom bombs dropped on Hiroshima and Nagasaki. However one views the use of the atom bombs, the governments of the United States and Japan wisely set up a system for carefully and extensively investigating the survivors and their children. In numbers, this represents the largest study of this kind.

An examination of this study, still in progress, illustrates the difficulties confronting geneticists. First, the dosages can only be estimated so that any relation between dose and effect cannot be exactly measured. Given the position of the parents at the time of the bombing and the approximate amount of shielding from buildings, etc., individuals have been grouped into five levels of exposure. Another problem is what should be observed in the offspring. One might look for an increase in traits known to be the result of dominant genes and whose spontaneous mutation rates had been estimated. Since the personnel and facilities required for such a study would be very great and since the estimated exposure doses were very low compared to those used in studies with other organisms, this method was not applicable.

Another approach is to look for general effects that might be the result of genetic changes. The frequencies of stillbirths, neonatal deaths, deaths during the first nine months after birth, congenital malformations, birthweight, and impaired physical development at nine months were investigated. A total of 73,362 infants were observed and 21,788 children re-examined at nine months. None of the above factors showed a significant difference of frequency between the control and experimental groups.

One other factor was investigated: the sex ratio at birth. Normally about 52% of births are boys to about 48% girls. In two control groups, the percentage of boys was 52.07 and 52.12%. In the groups exposed to the various levels of irradiation, a further distinction was made as to whether the father or the mother or both parents were exposed. About 19,000 births were included in these groups over a period of seven years.

After an accumulation of numbers, the scientist is faced with the problem of analysis. Just a flat increase or decrease can be the result of chance fluctuations, which is presumably the reason for the difference of 0.05% in the two control groups mentioned above. In the groups including both parents exposed, the frequency of males varied from 46.51% out of 43 births in which the mother had a high level of exposure and the father a moderate dose to 58.64% out of 220 births in which the mother had a low dose and the father a high dose. Also the size of sample varies greatly, from 33 births to parents both of whom were exposed to the highest level of irradiation to 5,994 births to parents each receiving the lowest exposure. The analysis of such data requires statistical methods which cannot be discussed here.

General trends were noted. In the cases where only the father was exposed, the proportion of male births per 100 units of dose showed an increase. In all but one group where the mother was exposed, the proportion of males showed a decrease. Statistically, however, in only one case, that of one group of maternal exposure, was the difference significant.

Even after analysis, it is the researcher who must reach some conclusions. In the case of Muller's experiments in 1927, the conclusions were obvious and not questioned. In this last material presented, the conclusions are not clear-cut and there is still much discussion among scientists. Based upon the statistical analysis, accepting the methods used, one can say that no genetic effect of radiation on man, including the sex-ratio, has been demonstrated. Some scientists have attempted to statistically analyze all the data grouped together; they maintain that when this is done, the change in sex-ratio is statistically significant. Some have said that although the results may not show significance mathematically, the general trends do suggest a genetic effect.

Neel has offered an explanation of how exposed males might have more sons and exposed mothers fewer sons. If the **Y** chromosome is relatively inert genetically, it would be less affected by irradiation than the **X** chromosome, which might have deleterious dominant and semidominant lethal mutations. The eggs receiving the **Y** chromosome from the exposed father would be less affected than the eggs receiving the **X** chromosome from the father, the effect on the other chromosomes being equal. Thus more sons would be expected. In the case of the exposed mothers having two **X** chromosomes, the sons receiving only one of them would be expected to be subject to sex-linked recessive lethal mutations. The daughters having two **X**'s, one from the exposed mother and one from the unexposed father, would not have this effect. Thus the number of sons would be expected to decrease. Moreover, when both parents are exposed, some factors affecting the birth rate of sons might be balanced by factors affecting the birth rate of daughters, so that these factors would tend to balance each other out with respect to the sex-ratio.

If such lethal mutations are occurring, one would expect fewer children. But to look for such an effect, particularly in humans, is fraught with difficulties. For example, in studies of families having lost children as a result of the Rh factor, more pregnancies than normal occur. Such families tend to try to overcompensate by having more children than the average if possible.

Perhaps the one conclusion to be reached is that more research on the genetic effects of radiation both on humans and other organisms is needed and, in fact, this is being done. In Hiroshima and Nagasaki, grandchildren of exposed individuals are now beginning to be born and it is hoped that enough money and facilities are made available for continued study.

Recently work has been done concerning the effect of radiation over several generations. An accumulation of lethal mutations with an increase in dose over generations has been shown in fruitflies. The results of similar research with mammals, mainly mice, is not clear. In the report of a recent symposium, "The Effects of Radiation on the Hereditary Fitness of Mammalian Populations," held in the summer of 1964, many of the problems of the design of experiments are pointed out. In the case of many mammals, there is difficulty in insuring that the only difference between the control and experimental groups is exposure to irradiation. They might have to be widely separated to be sure the control group is not exposed to irradiation. The temperature, or bacteria in the room or building, or even the treatment by laboratory personnel might differ. In trying to relate data to humans, it is suggested that animals having separate offspring such as chickens, rather than litter-bearing mammals, might be better research organisms.

Perhaps the words of J. L. Lush * quoted in the summary of the discussions at the symposium express the most appropriate attitude of the research scientist:

Otherwise, I think we are somewhat in that stage from 1918 to 1927. I think we do have some expectation on the basis of what we know about irradiation and life. We do expect there will be mutations, but we haven't got our techniques to where we can corner the evidence at least to the extent of making it of statistical significance. We haven't got it tied up.

* Genetics, 1964, 50: pp. 1216-1217.

chapter seven

The Genes

For most of this book the gene has been considered primarily as a unit of transmission. Ways and means of discovering patterns of inheritance were the main aims of early geneticists. Obviously there are other aspects of the gene that need to be studid. Chapter 6 dealt with the ability of genes to change. Two further questions have been intriguing scientists. What is the physical nature of genes? How is the final phenotype accomplished? Although such questions have been discussed since the beginning of genetics, it is the work of the past two or three decades that has produced some answers and a working hypothesis which is the basis of current research.

The approach to studying the nature and action of genes is quite different from studies of patterns of inheritance. In the latter case, the geneticist is usually concerned with mating individuals and the observation and counting of phenotypes. The individual methods have differed according to the reproductive structures of the organism used and the methods for discerning various phenotypes. In dealing with the problem of gene structure and action, the researcher is primarily concerned with chemical analysis of individuals of a given genotype and phenotype. This has meant that greater emphasis is placed upon the methods of chemistry and physics and has involved the development of techniques and the choice of organisms most suitable for such methods.

It is difficult to separate conclusions concerning the nature of genes and these concerning gene action, for they complement each other. Any concept of the nature of genes must explain both their own structure and what they are capable of doing.

Consider the choice of a suitable organism for the study of gene action. Ideally the effect of many genes should be easily available and clearly distinguishable. Many examples of the same genotype should be obtainable. Finally, one should be able to conclude that such traits are inherited and capable of analysis. Thus sexual reproduction and patterns of inheritance are important. But once these are established, the ability to study many individuals of the same and differing genotypes chemically becomes the primary aim of the geneticist.

Complex organisms such as man, corn, sweet peas and even fruitflies are difficult to use for such research. Microorganisms such as bacteria, molds and viruses are the main sources of information about gene action. One of the first microorganisms used was *Neurospora,* a pink mold that often grows on bread. It consists of long cellular filaments or hyphae forming a mat or mycelium of interwoven threads (Fig. 7-1). Some of the hyphae form small, round pink cells called conidiospores. This bread mold normally can grow on a relatively simple medium containing sugar, a nitrogen source, some inorganic acids and salts and one vitamin, biotin. Growth can be obtained from a piece of mycelium or from a conidiospore.

Neurospora also is able to reproduce sexually (Fig. 7-1). Only when two cultures look alike but are physiologically

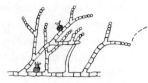

Mycelium of Mating Type A   Mycelium of Mating Type B

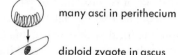
many asci in perithecium

diploid zygote in ascus

first meiotic division

two cells

second meiotic division

four cells

mitosis

eight haploid ascospores

mycelium from ascospore

FIGURE 7-1. Reproduction in *Neurospora*.

different are they able to mate. Each mating type forms a round, hollow ball of cells or protoperithecium with a few special hyphae at one end. Hyphae or conidiospores of the opposite mating type may fuse with these special hyphae. In the protoperithecium the two nuclei fuse, forming a diploid zygote in a sac or ascus. This cell undergoes meiosis forming four spores, each of which then divides mitotically, forming eight ascospores. Ripe perithecia can be broken open, releasing many asci. Using a low-power microscope and a fine glass or metal rod, each ascospore can be squeezed out of the ascus and grown separately. When put on suitable media, these ascospores form the hyphae and conidiospores of asexual reproduction.

Many inherited traits are known in *Neurospora:* mating type, color of conidia and of particular interest, biochemical mutants. The reason that this mold can normally grow on a simple medium is that it can make most of the materials it needs such as amino acids and vitamins, except biotin. During the 1940's, Beadle and Tatum described their method for obtaining and isolating such mutations.

Perithecia or conidiospores were exposed to x-rays or ultraviolet rays to induce mutations. The conidiospores were then allowed to fertilize hyphae of the opposite mating type, or the perithecia were allowed to develop. The resulting ascospores were isolated and grown in a test-tube on a medium containing many substances including amino acids, vitamins, sugars, etc. When mycelium formed on such complete medium, some of the hyphae were transferred to tubes of minimal media containing only those substances normally required by *Neurospora*. If they grew, it was concluded that a mutation had not occurred and that this was the normal unchanged mold. If, however, the hyphae did not grow on the minimal medium, it was concluded that a biochemical mutation had occurred which prevented the mold from making a particular substance. Then mycelium from the complete medium was transferred to tubes containing the minimal medium plus some added substances such as amino acids or vitamins. In this way the nature of the biochemical requirement could be narrowed down to a group. If, for instance, it did not grow in the tube with vitamins, more hyphae were transferred to tubes each containing the minimal medium plus one vitamin. In this way the requirement could be identified. One such biochemical mutant grew on complete medium and on minimal medium plus vitamin B_1. The mutant could be further characterized. Vitamin B_1 is composed of two main parts: thiazole and pyrimidine. Minimal medium plus thiazole supports growth of this mutant, but minimal medium plus pyrimidine does not. The conclusion is reached that this mutant can make pyrimidine but not thiazole, which must be added before growth can occur.

Each mutant also was crossed with normal strains and their inherited nature established. Additional crosses located each mutant as belonging to one of seven possible linkage groups.

The chemical reactions of a living organism are under the control of enzymes produced by that organism. Enzymes are specialized proteins acting as catalysts in increasing the rate of such chemical reactions and allowing them to occur in the environment of cells. Beadle and Tatum developed the one gene-one enzyme theory, namely that each gene has its effect by controlling the production of a specific enzyme. The design of their experiments was admirably suited for detecting such one gene-one enzyme relationships. In some cases a series of related reactions could be analyzed. Three mutants were obtained, all of which required the amino acid, arginine, to grow. These mutants were found by linkage studies to be located on the same chromosome, although this was not always the case of mutants requiring the same material. The action of these mutants, however, differed. One mutant grew if either ornithine, citrulline or arginine was supplied. A second mutant required either citrulline or arginine and the third survived only if arginine was added.

The sequence of steps under gene control is pictured as follows:

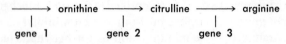

Thus the second mutant blocked the formation of citrulline from ornithine. If citrulline or arginine was supplied, this step was bypassed and the organism could grow. But supplying ornithine would still require this chemical reaction and the mold would not grow.

If a gene controlled more than one reaction, its detection was much more difficult. Just the right two or three or more substances would have to be added to the minimal medium to discover such mutants. Even if they were discovered, it still might be argued that more than one mutation had occurred or that there was still one primary gene effect. Also the direct relationship of a gene causing the formation or lack of formation of an enzyme is not easily nor clearly demonstrable. In one case, the enzyme whose action was blocked by a mutation was found to be present, but it was active only if the organism was kept at a low temperature and in less oxygen than usual. Certainly the relationship of a gene to a particular chemical reaction is clear, but the nature of this relationship is not always as obvious.

These studies of gene action involve the association of phenotypes, specific and biochemical in nature with mutations. Another approach is to attempt to study the characteristics of the gene. Early in genetics the association of genes with chromosomes was well established. First, staining techniques and later chemical analysis of isolated chromosomes indicated that these structures consist of two main substances, proteins and nucleic acids. The latter are of two types, deoxyribonucleic acid (DNA) and ribonucleic acid

(RNA). The structure of these nucleic acids will be presented later (p. 89). The question then becomes which of these three substances, protein, DNA, or RNA, is the basic composition of the gene.

The amount of protein and of RNA in the nuclei of cells varies considerably, whereas the amount of DNA is relatively stable for a given species. Moreover, the amount of DNA is generally correlated with the number of sets of chromosomes. Although there may be small variations in the amount of DNA, diploid cells with two sets of chromosomes have twice that in haploid cells with one set of chromosomes. This would suggest a relationship between genes and DNA. But two characteristics of genes must be accounted for in any hypothesis of gene structure. Genes are able to duplicate themselves. The large number of genes also requires a substance capable of great variation. At first the main part of DNA was thought to be a repetition of four units, limiting the variability of this substance. Proteins, on the other hand, were known to have many forms such as enzymes and hormones.

The direct demonstration in 1944 of the chemical nature of genetic material came from a study of what might first seem an unlikely subject, bacteria. Not until 1946 was genetic recombination or essentially sex demonstrated in bacteria, and chromosomes cannot be detected in many bacteria. Despite such seeming drawbacks, the result of the research of Avery, Macleod and McCarty is quite clear-cut. They used a round bacterium, the *Pneumococcus*. Some pneumococci have a capsule around the cell. Such cells, when grown on artificial media, form smooth (S-type) glistening colonies of many cells. When injected, such cells pause pneumonia in man and a fatal infection in mice. Another group of pneumococcal cells do not possess the capsule, form small rough (R-type) colonies and do not cause disease when injected.

The presence or absence of a capsule is an inherited trait and is usually typical of a particular strain. Encapsulated cells have been found to occasionally convert to rough non-encapsulated forms, but the reverse reaction (R to S) does not occur naturally. Such a change or transformation can be induced under specific conditions. Griffith found that mice injected with living R type II cells and heat-killed S type III cells often died from the infection and living S type III cells were obtainable. The cells were not brought to life, but R cells were transformed into specific S forms. In the early 30's, such transformations were accomplished in test-tubes. R cells were grown in fluid medium with serum containing antibodies against R cells. If either killed S cells or sterile extracts of S cells containing no cell parts was added, transformation of some the R cells into S cells occurred. Such transformed cells were stable, forming S cells for many generations. It was concluded that S cells produced a substance, the transforming principle, soluble in the medium and capable of inducing the inherited trait of forming a capsule.

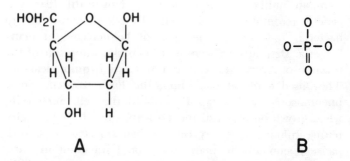

FIGURE 7-2. Two components of DNA. A = deoxyribose. B = phosphate group.

In 1944 this transforming substance was separated from S cell extract and purified. After making sure it could cause transformation, the substance was analyzed by various means, both chemical and enzymatic. Typical chemical tests for protein and sugar were negative and a test for RNA was weakly positive, which is often the case with purified preparations of known DNA. The amount of nitrogen to phosphorus was comparable to that postulated for DNA. Enzymes known to destroy proteins and RNA did not destroy the transforming ability of the substance. Other enzymes which destroyed known samples of DNA did stop the ability to transform R pneumococci. These and other tests estab-

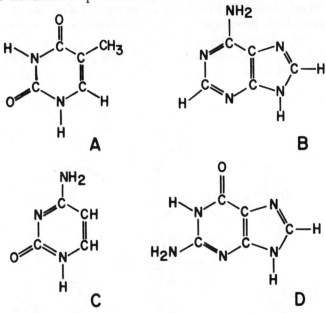

FIGURE 7-3. The nitrogen bases of DNA. Purines: A = thymine, B = cytosine. Pyrimidines: C = adenine, D = guanine.

lished DNA as the substance which endowed the cells with a specific inherited trait.

The question of how DNA could replicate itself and control basic reactions of cells was still to be hypothesized. In 1953 Watson and Crick gave the impetus for much research and postulations about these questions. They presented what they thought the DNA molecule was like, a structure allowing for replication.

Basically DNA has three component parts: deoxyribose, a sugar; a phosphate group; and nitrogen bases (Figs. 7-2 and 7-3). The nitrogen bases are of four kinds: cytosine and thymine, both hexagonal compounds called pyrimidines; and guanine and adenine, the larger purines (Fig. 7-3). DNA always is made up of equal amounts of adenine and thymine and of cytosine and guanine. A union of a nitrogen base with a sugar molecule is called a nucleoside. The larger unit of a nucleoside and a phosphate is a nucleotide (Fig. 7-4).

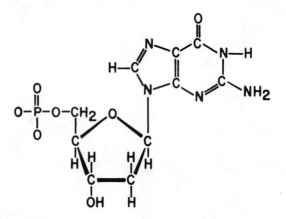

FIGURE 7-4. A nucleotide, the basic unit of DNA. It is composed of a union of a nitrogen base, guanine in this case, deoxyribose and phosphate.

When x-rays are passed through molecules of a crystalline substance, the various parts of the molecule diffract them at specific angles depending upon the position and size of the parts of the molecule. From such x-ray diffraction studies, Watson and Crick suggested the following general structural arrangement of DNA. The sugar-phosphate units form two long chains. The two chains are linked to each other by means of a series of nitrogen bases. Adenine is always linked with thymine and cytosine with guanine. Furthermore, the two chains form a double helix (Fig. 7-5). It is hypothesized

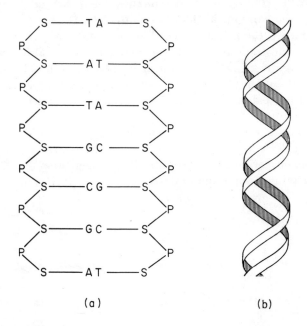

(a)   (b)

FIGURE 7-5. (a) A diagram of a short chain of DNA. S = deoxyribo, P = phosphate, C = cytosine, G = guanine, A = adenine, T = thymine, (b) A double helix.

that in order to duplicate, the DNA molecule separates into two single chains, each chain able to synthesize a copy of the other one, the two old and new chains uniting to form two molecules of DNA. Thus the order of nitrogen bases controls the synthesis of new DNA. In Fig. 7-5 one part of a chain of the DNA has the nitrogen bases in the order T-A-T-G-C-C. Presumably this chain could control the formation of a single strand of DNA with the bases in the order of A-T-A-C-G-G, these two uniting to form the whole DNA molecule or part of it, since this represents only a very small fraction of an entire molecule. There may be three to four thousand nucleotides in a molecule of DNA.

This is the picture of DNA which can explain its structure and replication. But such a picture must also satisfy the ability of DNA to control cellular reactions. DNA is found only in the nuclei of cells. Thus there must be a substance capable of many various forms which can be made by DNA and found in both the chromosomes and cytoplasm of cells. Ribonucleic acid is just such a substance. It differs from DNA in three ways. The sugar molecule, ribose, differs from deoxyribose in having an added oxygen atom (Fig. 7-6). Thymine is not found in RNA but another purine, uracil, is

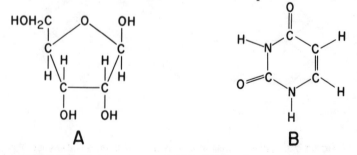

FIGURE 7-6. The components of RNA differing from DNA. A = ribose. B = uracil.

(Fig. 7-6). Finally, it usually is present in a single chain, the nitrogen bases being free at one end. This is not always true of some forms of RNA.

The current hypothesis of gene action is as follows. RNA is synthesized by DNA similar to its mode of self-replication, adenine now linking up uracil. Probably only one strand of the DNA molecule does this. This RNA is released into the cytoplasm. There is evidence for three types of RNA in the cytoplasm based on their structure, particularly length, and stability. There definitely are two types having very distinct functions. Short double chains of RNA called transfer RNA (sRNA) are capable of linking up with specific amino acids, the building blocks of proteins and also of enzymes. This ability to combine with a specific amino acid is under the control of an enzyme. Many such units of sRNA-amino acid are carried to particular structures in cells, the ribosomes which contain a very stable form of RNA. The sRNA-amino acid units can combine with messenger RNA (mRNA), larger molecules formed by the DNA and found in the cytoplasm. When mRNA is free, it is quite unstable. These messenger molecules somehow govern the order and so control the combination of amino acids into polypeptides which when combined form proteins. Thus the mRNA is said to carry the coding message from the DNA and to carry out the primary function of genes.

It is difficult to choose experiments to illustrate the methods used in finding evidence concerning this theory. They are complex and involved, often requiring much background information. Moreover, the research is extremely current and many of the detailed steps of the actions of DNA and the various kinds of RNA are still to be clearly and definitely established.

One approach is to determine the relationship between

the nucleotides, particularly the nitrogen bases, adenine, uracil, cytosine and guanine, of RNA and the formation of proteins. All proteins are combinations of amino acids, of which there are over twenty. This means that the arrangement of the four nitrogen bases somehow guides the arrangement of the amino acids into proteins. A primary question is how many nitrogen bases are related to one amino acid. The minimum number can be determined without experiment. If each nitrogen base (A, U, G, C) controlled one amino acid, there could only be four amino acids regulated. Obviously this is not enough. If any two nitrogen bases (UU, AA, GG, CC, UA, AU, UG, GU, etc.) controlled one amino acid, there are sixteen (4 x 4) possible combinations, still not a sufficient number. If the code is in units of three bases (UUU, GGG, UGU, AGU, etc.), there are 64 (4 x 4 x 4) possibilities. Consequently, the minimum coding unit is three nitrogen bases.

Many attempts to determine the specific codes have been and are being made. An early experiment reported by Nirenberg and Matthaei in 1961 illustrates some of the methods used. Basically, a mixture of substances including ribosomes, sRNA, synthesized or natural mRNA and amino acids was analyzed for the presence of proteins and their chemical nature was determined.

The preparation of all the substances used cannot be described, but the general preparation of the ribosomes will give some idea of what is involved. Cells of a bacterium, *E. coli,* are ground up in a fluid. This breaks up the cells. This mixture is put in a centrifuge and spun around at a relatively low speed. The heavy intact cells settle to the bottom and are discarded. The fluid left, or supernatant, is then combined with an enzyme which destroys DNA. Again this is centrifuged at slightly higher speeds and the supernatant is saved. The fluid is centrifuged at a much higher speed which causes the ribosomes to fall to the bottom of the tube. Other substances such as sRNA are still in the fluid portion. The sediment and fluid are separated. The ribosomes in the sediment are washed and recentrifuged ready to be used as part of the test mixture. Much of the preparation of such materials depends upon the use of enzymes to destroy unwanted material and upon centrifugation at different speeds, causing the sedimentation and layering of different substances depending upon their size and weight.

It was found that messenger RNA, ribosomes and an energy source were required for the incorporation of amino acids into protein. Transfer sRNA stimulated this incorporation. A very significant observation was that when synthetic messenger mRNA composed of many uracil units was used, a specific amino acid, phenylalanine, was transformed into protein. The conclusion is that UUU is the code for this amino acid. Much similar research has led to the identification, some still tentative, of the code or codes for the twenty amino acids.

This entire area of investigation of the nature, action and relationships of DNA, various RNA's, amino acids and proteins has burgeoned to such an extent that what might be called a "new" field of biology, molecular biology, has been established. Whether it really is a new field or not may be questioned, but many universities and research laboratories now have departments or institutes of molecular biology.

But what of the gene of genetics? The concept of the gene has undergone an interesting evolution. The gene has been considered a unit of transmission which has a specific function resulting in a particular phenotype and which is capable of change or mutation. If these characteristics are considered separately as to how they are determined and their possible relation to DNA structure is postulated, it will be found that the one word, gene, is not enough.

The unit of transmission, the allele, is recognized by the lack of crossing over. Non-allelic genes which are linked show some segregation, being on homologous chromosomes, but also some degree of recombination. Alleles, however, always segregate. This then is the basis of the smallest unit which is transmitted from one generation to the next.

If we consider the picture of a functioning unit compared to the transmitted unit, some discrepancies occur. The existence of pseudoalleles discussed in Chapter 5 is pertinent. These are closely linked "genes," but separable by recombination. Each pseudoallele results in the same or extremely similar phenotypes. Moreover, their relative positions influence their functioning. Two types of double heterozygotes are possible (see page 51). When the normal pseudoalleles are on the same chromosome, the *cis* position (+ +/a b) the phenotype is normal. In the *trans* position of the pseudo-alleles, being on different chromosomes (+ b/a +), the non-normal phenotype is expressed. This and other evidences have led to the realization that the functional unit, the smallest unit resulting in a particular phenotype, need not necessarily be exactly comparable to the unit of transmission. Similarly, the smallest unit of change resulting in a mutation need not be the same as the other units.

As a result, three new words have been established: recon, cistron, and muton to designate the three interpretations of the word gene. It is not always wise to add words to a subject already abounding in technical terms. In this case the introduction of these terms has been very useful in enabling geneticists to clarify their answers to "What is a gene?"

In postulating the relation of these "genes" to DNA,

many possibilities exist. In the case of the muton, an example in man has been very helpful. Sickle-cell anemia is a disease which is inherited and which results in the formation of abnormal hemoglobin. Hemoglobin is an iron-containing protein which occurs in red blood cells and functions in the transport of oxygen. Sickle-cell anemia is the result of a recessive gene (recon?) which, when homozygous, causes the formation of sickle-shaped red blood cells and severe anemia. Heterozygous individuals have sickle-shaped cells but no anemia. The hemoglobin of anemic individuals differs from that of normal persons. Heterozygotes have about equal amounts of the two kinds of hemoglobin, which are separable. Analysis has shown that the two hemoglobins differ from each other *only* in one amino acid. The other amino acids, about 500 of them, are alike in the two hemoglobin proteins. Presumably when a normal gene mutates to the sickle-cell allele, the effect is to change one amino acid of a particular protein.

It has been postulated that the sequence of the nitrogen bases, such as UUU, in mRNA controls the incorporation of a particular amino acid into protein. The structure of that mRNA, including the sequence of such three bases, is under the control of DNA and its sequence of purines and pyrimidines. A change in one nitrogen base, such as AAA to ATA, would change the structure of the mRNA formed from UUU to UAU in this case. This change in the code could change the one amino acid in a protein. Thus a muton or gene, as a unit of change, could be one nucleotide.

A particular protein, like hemoglobin, is the result of hundreds of amino acids in a specific order. Such a phenotype would require many nitrogen base codes and so many nucleotides of DNA. The cistron, or gene as a unit of function, would be larger than a muton. The estimate of a recon is very difficult. Conclusions drawn from work with viruses indicate that a recon is more comparable in size to a muton.

As research has continued, the concept of the gene has changed with the ability to be more precise and comprehending. Genetics has come a long way since the factors of Mendel were rediscovered only sixty-five years ago.

chapter eight

Genetics and Biology

The knowledge of any field of biology has ramifications and significance for other areas of study. To a very great extent this is true of genetics. Although the primary concern of this book has been genetics as a specific isolated endeavor, a brief discussion of the role of genetics in some other disciplines is in order.

Cytology is the study of cells, their structure and functioning. Obviously since DNA, RNA, and chromosomes are integral parts of cells, these two areas have become interdependent. Many examples of such interdependency already have been presented. Genetics, itself, could not have progressed as it has without the previous work of the cytologist.

If the genetic material is the regulatory mechanism for the development and differentiation of cells, embryology, too, must draw upon genetics. It is this area that has presented biologists with a most intriguing question. Mitosis involves the exact replication of DNA and equal distribution into daughter cells. This means such cells must all be genetically alike. If the chromosomes and genetic material of all diploid cells of a developing organism result from mitosis, how are cells able to differentiate into different tissues and organs? The answer has come from developmental genetics. In general, gene action is dependent upon the cellular environment of the genetic material just as the cells are dependent upon the genetic material. The elucidation of this situation has involved a variety of approaches and is presented in another book of this series, "Developmental Genetics."

The field that has been influenced perhaps the most by genetics is organic evolution. In 1859, six years before Mendel, Darwin published "The Origin of Species." Briefly stated, he presented the idea that species adapted to their environment developed from pre-existing less specialized species. Variations which are inherited occur in species. Some of these variations make the individuals possessing them better able to survive and have offspring in a given environment. Thus nature or the environment selects out those organisms which possess advantageous inherited characteristics. Eventually such variations accumulate so that the organisms differ from their ancestors to the extent of being a new species. Without any other details or evidence, it is clear that such a theory would be greatly influenced by genetics. Genes and their mutations provide the very source for the inherited variations which Darwin recognized must be an integral part of evolution.

Genetics in turn has influenced some of our ideas of organic evolution. Species are, after all, populations of individuals. What happens to that population genetically influences its evolution. The whole field of population genetics with its own methods and conclusions has evolved. For example, it can be shown mathematically that if there are no forces affecting the frequency of a gene in a freely interbreeding population the frequency of each allele tends to remain constant from generation to generation. Much of evolutionary study has become one of studying those forces which can influence the gene frequency in a population. If a population of individuals is a mixture of tall and short persons and the members of the group mate at random, the frequency of alleles for tallness and shortness would remain constant and the population would not change. Many factors might influence the make-up of such a population. If tall individuals tended to choose other tall individuals, such preferential mating would influence the frequency of the genes, genotypes, and phenotypes. A change would also occur if, for any reason, the number of offspring of two tall parents tended to be greater than the average family, and survived.

How selection acts against or for particular types of inheritance also is significant. If a dominant gene causes a defect to the extent of causing death before reproductive age, any individual with that gene is eliminated as far as contributing genetically to the next generation is concerned. Any new appearance of the gene must be the result of mutation. A defect which is the result of a recessive gene has a very different history. The homozygote will not survive or contribute to the next generation, but the gene can remain in the population in heterozygotes. Each type of inheritance has its own pattern of influence. Until recently, people with hemophilia died at an early age. Since it is sex-linked, the gene was kept in the population as a result of mutation and in the heterozygous condition in females, but hemophiliac males were what is called genetic deaths. Since medical science has enabled people with hemophilia to live much longer, the frequency of this gene in humans may change.

Obviously then, genetics and the study of evolution are inseparable. Physical anthropology, the study of the organic evolution of man, must also be allied to genetics. Human genetics has supplied many additional traits, such as blood groups, with which to study the races of man. The influence that man may have upon his own evolution has been the concern of many geneticists, anthropologists and other individuals. The influence of medical science upon hemophilia, described above, is only one such example. The concern over radiation and its genetic effects is largely one of what effect it will have on future generations of man and other organisms.

An exciting although relatively unexplored area is the relation of psychology and genetics. Chapter 6 dealt with traits which are the result of many genes. Studies of identical and fraternal twins discussed in that chapter indicate that many traits, such as intelligence and temperament, are inherited to some degree. The field of behavioral genetics is a difficult one, involving the handicaps discussed in Chapter 6 and others as well. The identification of the multiple genic inheritance involved in such traits is compounded by the strong influence of the environment and by the problem of quantitatively and accurately measuring such characteristics. How does one measure how excitable an individual is? Such traits are of interest to us primarily in man, but humans usually are not the best subjects for genetic research. Recently more attempts have been made to study the genetics of behavior in other animals such as dogs, mice and even flatworms. This requires the mutual cooperation and understanding of geneticists, psychologists, and often statisticians.

In the relatively few years of its existence, not only has genetics progressed rapidly in its own right but it has caused equal repercussions in many other areas. It will be exciting to see what the second half-century of its life will bring.

Suggested References

Three sources of original papers in genetics are

CLASSIC PAPERS IN GENETICS, ed. J. A. Peters, Prentice-Hall, Englewood Cliffs, N.J. 1959.

PAPERS ON HUMAN GENETICS, ed. S. H. Boyer, Prentice-Hall, Englewood Cliffs, N. J. 1963.

STUDIES IN GENETICS, H. J. Muller, Indiana University Press, Bloomington, Indiana. 1962.

A few of many texts of genetics are

CELL HEREDITY, R. Sager and F. J. Ryan, Wiley, New York. 1961.

ELEMENTARY GENETICS, W. R. Singleton, D. Van Nostrand, New York. 1962.

GENETICS, I. Herskowitz, Little, Brown, Boston. 1965.

PRINCIPLES OF GENETICS, E. W. Sinnott, L. C. Dunn, and T. Dobzhansky, McGraw-Hill, New York. 1958.

PRINCIPLES OF HUMAN GENETICS, C. Stern, W. H. Freeman, San Francisco. 1960.

SPIRIN, RNA, Reinhold Pub. Corp. 1964.

Many excellent articles may be found in issues of *Scientific American*.

Glossary

Alleles (allelomorphs). Alternative forms of a gene which occupy the same position in homologous chromosomes and which segregate during meiosis.

Amino acid. An organic acid containing an amino group, NH_2. Many linked amino acids form a protein.

Antibody. A substance, usually protein, whose formation is induced by the presence of an antigen. The anti-A and anti-B antibodies seem to be an exception, the antibodies being present although the antigens are not. Antigens and antibodies specifically and physically unite when together.

Antigen. A substance, usually protein, which, when introduced into an organism, will induce the formation of antibodies.

Apogamy. The formation of a diploid plant without fertilization.

Ascospore. One of the eight haploid spores formed in the asci of certain fungi.

Ascus. The sac of a particular group of fungi (Ascomycetes), including *Neurospora*, in which haploid spores form as a result of meiosis.

Autosomes. Chromosomes other than sex chromosomes.

Backcross. Mating an individual with one parent.

Blood groups. The classification of individuals based upon the presence of specific antigens on the red blood cells. The **ABO** group is the best known. Other groups include the **MN** group and the **Rh** factors.

Carrier. An individual who is heterozygous for a recessive gene and so does not show its presence.

Chromosome. A rod shaped body found in the nuclei of cells and carrying the units of heredity. The number is characteristic of a species. In diploid cells there are pairs of like chromosomes.

Cis position. The location in a heterozygote of closely linked mutant alleles on the same chromosome, the normal alleles being on the other homologous chromosome.

Continuous variation. Differences which form an uninterrupted range of measurements, i.e., height.

Corolla. The petals of a flower joined together into a floral envelope.

Cross-fertilization. The union of two gametes, each from a different individual.

Crossing over. The exchange of chromatin material, including linked genes, between homologous chromosomes during meiosis.

Deletion. The loss of a part of a chromosome.

Diploid. Having two sets of chromosomes.

Discontinuous variation. Differences which can be classified into distinct categories, i.e., red or white petals.

DNA. Deoxyribonucleic acid. A large molecule made up of nucleotides in two strands forming a double helix. The basic functioning substance of the gene.

Dominant gene. A gene which can suppress the expression of an allele.

Drosophila (fruitfly). A small two-winged insect often found around fruit.

E. coli. A bacterium commonly found in the intestines of many animals. It is used in the study of molecular genetics including the study of the genetics of viruses which infect it.

Effective gene. In polygenic inheritance those genes which contribute to the phenotype of the individual.

Enzyme. A protein which catalyzes specific chemical reactions in organisms. Genes are believed to produce their effects by controlling the formation of enzymes.

Erythroblastosis fetalis. An anemia of new born infants sometimes resulting from the mother producing antibodies against antigens of the child's red blood cells as in "Rh babies."

F_1. First filial generation. Usually refers to the offspring of unlike homozygous parents.

F_2. Second filial generation. Refers to the offspring of F_1 parents.

Fertilization. The union of two gametes to form a diploid zygote.

Gamete. A germ cell, usually haploid. In bisexual reproduction two gametes fuse to form the diploid zygote of the next generation. In animals eggs and sperm are the gametes. In higher plants the egg and part of the pollen are the gametes.

Gene   (factor). Unit of heredity. See last chapter for distinction of unit of transmission, unit of mutation, and unit of physiooligical action.

Generation   (generation time). Average period from formation of parent to formation of offspring. In some bacteria this is 20 minutes; in fruitflies, 10–12 days; and in man, 25 years.

Genotype. The gene make-up of an organism.

Germ cells. See **Gametes.**

Haploid. Having one set of chromosomes.

Hemizygous. Having only one allele or chromosome.

Hemophilia. A sex-linked trait in man in which the blood does not clot readily.

Heterosis. See **Hybrid vigor.**

Heterozygous. Having two different alleles. Two types of gametes form.

Homologous chromosomes   (homologs). Chromosomes which are alike in size, shape, and function and which pair, point for point, during meiosis.

Homozygous. Having two like alleles so that only one type of gamete is formed.

Hybrid. The offspring of unlike parents. A monohybrid has parents differing with respect to one pair of genes. A dihybrid has parents differing with respect to two pairs of genes.

Hybrid vigor (**heterosis**). Unusual growth and healthiness of organisms resulting from the crossing of two unrelated, less vigorous parents.

Hypha (pl. **hyphae**). The thread-like element of the mycelium of a fungus.

Identical twins. Twins resulting from one fertilized egg divided into two zygotes. Non-identical or fraternal twins result from two fertilized eggs developing at the same time.

Inbreeding. The mating of closely related individuals. Self-fertilization is the highest degree of inbreeding. Inbreeding increases the degree of homozygosity.

Linkage maps. Location of linked genes based upon proportion of crossing over.

Linked genes. Genes located on the same chromosome and showing a specific percentage of crossing over proportional to their distance from each other.

Locus (pl. **loci**). Physical position of a gene on a chromosome. Alleles occupy the same locus.

Marker genes. Genes whose effect and position are known. Used in controlled studies of other genes.

Meiosis. A special type of cell division involving two cell divisions and resulting in cells having one-half the original number of chromosomes.

Minimal medium. Nutrient materials containing only those substances known to be needed for growth. Used in biochemical studies of *Neurospora*.

Multiple alleles. More than two alleles at a given locus.

Mutagen. A physical or chemical substance which can cause genes to mutate.

Mutant. An inherited phenotype differing from the normal or wild type.

Mutation. A stable inherited change. Usually means a gene change. May mean a chromosomal change.

Mycelium (pl. **mycelia**). The network of filaments which result from the growth of a fungus.

Neurospora. A fungus commonly found as a pink mold on bread.

Non-disjunction. The failure of two homologous chromosomes to separate during meiosis and resulting in one daughter cell having both chromosomes, the other daughter cell having none.

Nucleoside. The union of a nitrogen base and a sugar molecule. A subunit of **DNA** and **RNA**.

Nucleotide. The union of a nitrogen base, a sugar, and a phosphate. A subunit of **DNA** and **RNA**.

Nucleus. A structure found in cells, separated from the rest of the cell by a membrane and containing chromosomes.

Outbreeding (**outcrossing**). Mating of unrelated individuals.

Overdominance. The heterozygote having a greater effect than the homozygous dominant.

Perithecium. A spherical or flask-shaped hollow structure containing many asci.

Phenotype. The appearance of an organism as a result of its genotype and environment.

Polygenic inheritance. Quantitative traits resulting from the action of many non-allelic genes.

Position effect. The physical arrangement of genes influencing their phenotype.

Protoperithecium. An immature perithecium.

Pseudoalleles. Genes which seem to be alleles affecting the same characteristic but which show crossing over and so are closely linked non-alleles.

Purine. A type of nitrogen base. Adenine and guanine are the purines found in **DNA** and **RNA**.

Pyrimidine. A type of nitrogen base including cytosine and thymine found in **DNA** and cytosine and uracil found in **RNA**.

Quantitative inheritance. See **Polygenic inheritance.**

Random assortment. The coming together by chance.

Recessive gene. A gene whose expression is suppressed by a dominant allele.

Reciprocal crosses. Two matings in which the sex of the types of parents is reversed.

RNA. Ribonucleic acid. A large molecule made up of nucleotides as a single coiled strand. Thought to be formed by **DNA** and differing from it in the type of sugar and one of the nitrogen bases making up the nucleotides.

Salivary gland. A structure found in the larvae of some insects including *Drosophila*. It has cells with very large nuclei and chromosomes.

Segregation. Separation. Alleles segregate during meiosis forming different gametes.

Self-fertilization. The union of two gametes each from the same individual. Common in plants.

Sex chromosomes. Chromosomes particularly related to sex determination. Sexes have a different complement of sex chromosomes. In *Drosophila* and man the females have two **X** chromosomes, the males one **X** and one **Y** chromosome.

Sickle-cell anemia. An inherited trait in man resulting in abnormal hemoglobin being formed. The red blood cells are sickle shaped when under reduced oxygen tension.

Spontaneous mutation. A gene change resulting from no known cause. Artificially induced mutations are the result of the application of a mutagen.

Standard deviation. A statistic which measures the degree of variation from the average.

Synapsis. The pairing, point for point, of homologous chromosomes during meiosis.

Testcross. The mating of an individual with a recessive organism to discover if the individual is homozygous or heterozygous.

Transforming principle. A substance, now known to be **DNA**, found in cell extracts which can specifically change the genotype of a microorganism.

Trans position. The location, in a heterozygote, of closely linked mutant alleles being on different homologous chromosomes.

Wild type. The normal phenotype.

X chromosome. A sex chromosome. One sex will have two **X**'s as in female *Drosophila* and male chickens and the other sex will have one **X**.

Y chromosome. A sex chromosome found in the males of many organisms. **Y** chromosomes usually have very few, if any, genes.

Zygote. The individual, usually diploid, which results from the union of two gametes. The zygote then becomes the embryo and finally the adult of the next generation.

Index

Numbers in *italic* indicate figures.